· BEST EVER
CROSSWORDS
Unleash your inner genius

igloobooks

igloobooks

Published in 2021
First published in the UK by Igloo Books Ltd
An imprint of Igloo Books Ltd
Cottage Farm, NN6 0BJ, UK
Owned by Bonnier Books
Sveavägen 56, Stockholm, Sweden
www.igloobooks.com

0321 004
4 6 8 10 9 7 5
ISBN 978-1-83852-194-3

Cover designed by Dave Chapman

Puzzle compilation, typesetting and design by:
Clarity Media Ltd, http://www.clarity-media.co.uk

Printed and manufactured in China

Contents

No. 1

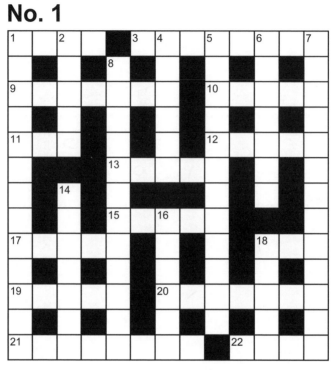

Across

1	Annoying person (4)
3	Clamber (8)
9	Frozen water spears (7)
10	Ascend (5)
11	Food item from a hen (3)
12	Speak in a slow manner (5)
13	Venerate; worship (5)
15	Completely correct (5)
17	Data entered into a system (5)
18	Tree (3)
19	Invigorating medicine (5)
20	Plunder (7)
21	Uneasy (8)
22	Opposite of right (4)

Down

1	Head of the government (5,8)
2	Smart; ache (5)
4	Gambling house (6)
5	Not on purpose; inadvertently (12)
6	Great ___ : island (7)
7	Ornamentation (13)
8	Pertaining to letters (12)
14	Grows larger (7)
16	Changes (6)
18	With speed (5)

No. 2

Across

1	Enumerates (6)
4	Heading on a document (6)
9	Country in NW Africa (7)
10	Becomes fully grown (7)
11	___ Presley: US singer (5)
12	Became less intense (5)
14	Ashley ___ : actress (5)
15	Facial protuberances (5)
17	Cereal plant (5)
18	Pasta pockets (7)
20	Tenth month of the year (7)
21	Unrefined (6)
22	Silver (literary) (6)

Down

1	Force to do something (6)
2	Straightens out (8)
3	Small nails (5)
5	Indefinitely many (7)
6	Lion noise (4)
7	Opposite of open (6)
8	Eg a piece of music (11)
13	Capable of being satisfied (8)
14	Diffusion of molecules through a membrane (7)
15	Scandinavian (6)
16	Kept private; unknown by others (6)
17	A thing that measures (5)
19	Document allowing entry to a country (4)

No. 3

Across

- 1 Initiators (11)
- 9 Circle a planet (5)
- 10 Issue legal proceedings (3)
- 11 Ring-shaped object (5)
- 12 Random number game (5)
- 13 Culinary herb (8)
- 16 German motorway (8)
- 18 Wipe (5)
- 21 Refine metal (5)
- 22 Female sheep (3)
- 23 Make a map of (5)
- 24 Designed for usefulness (11)

Down

- 2 Closest (7)
- 3 Couple (7)
- 4 Speak unintelligibly (6)
- 5 Sum; add up (5)
- 6 Restore factory settings (5)
- 7 Explained the meaning of (11)
- 8 Divisor (11)
- 14 Support or strengthen (7)
- 15 ___ Hudgens: High School Musical star (7)
- 17 Diacritical mark of two dots (6)
- 19 Good at (5)
- 20 Do really well at (5)

No. 4

Across

1 Bends (6)
7 Tanks for storing water (8)
8 Mythical monster (3)
9 US state of islands (6)
10 Sailing vessel (4)
11 Tripod for an artist (5)
13 Itemising (7)
15 Cattle herders (7)
17 Scraped at (5)
21 Hoist (4)
22 Have as a purpose (6)
23 Large deer (3)
24 Use something to maximum advantage (8)
25 Tin alloy (6)

Down

1 Select (6)
2 Material wealth (6)
3 Discard; throw away (5)
4 Drug that relieves pain (7)
5 Feud (8)
6 Issue instructions; order (6)
12 Cause resentment (8)
14 Expressive (of music) (7)
16 Small oval fruits (6)
18 Broadest (6)
19 Labourer at a port (6)
20 Sharply inclined (5)

No. 5

Across

1 Painful or aching (4)
3 Skin care product (8)
9 Perennial plant with fleshy roots (7)
10 Suppress (5)
11 Significant (12)
14 Bat (anag) (3)
16 Unfasten (5)
17 Increase the running speed of an engine (3)
18 Act of discussing something; deliberation (12)
21 Movable joint a door swings on (5)
22 Influences that contribute to a result (7)
23 Transient (8)
24 Extravagant publicity (4)

Down

1 Wisdom (8)
2 Angry dispute (3-2)
4 Limb used for walking (3)
5 Person one knows (12)
6 Pertaining to the stars (7)
7 Actor's part in a film (4)
8 Having a tendency to become liquid (12)
12 Kick out (5)
13 Fade away (8)
15 Small chewy chocolate cake (7)
19 Form of humour (5)
20 Cook (4)
22 Wetland (3)

No. 6

Across

1 Tempestuous (6)
5 Mischievous sprite (3)
7 Protective garment worn in the kitchen (5)
8 Appropriate (7)
9 Observed (5)
10 Prohibit (8)
12 Former students (6)
14 Cave openings (6)
17 State of remaining alive (8)
18 Shallow recess (5)
20 First light (7)
21 Staggers (5)
22 Male child (3)
23 Layers (anag) (6)

Down

2 Insignificant (7)
3 Core mass of a country (8)
4 Type of golf club (4)
5 A precise point in time (7)
6 Very fine substances (7)
7 Softly radiant (5)
11 Persuade (8)
12 Streets (7)
13 Imaginary creature (7)
15 Gossip (7)
16 Speculate (5)
19 Flat and smooth (4)

CROSSWORD

No. 7

Across

1 Miserly (6)
4 Restraint (6)
9 Connoisseur (7)
10 Distributing (7)
11 Happening (5)
12 Survived (5)
14 Nonsense (5)
15 Call forth (5)
17 Roman cloaks (5)
18 Japanese warriors (7)
20 Make obsolete (7)
21 Sculptured symbols (6)
22 Type of petrol (6)

Down

1 Make less hard (6)
2 An indirect implication (8)
3 Remorse (5)
5 Letter (7)
6 Sound system (2-2)
7 Girded (anag) (6)
8 A cause of great trouble (11)
13 Front of an advancing army (8)
14 Expecting prices to fall (7)
15 Relaxing; diminishing (6)
16 Go up (6)
17 Levy (5)
19 Numerous (4)

No. 8

CROSSWORD

Across

1 Totally erase (4)
3 Enter unlawfully (8)
9 Saviour (7)
10 Wide-awake (5)
11 Written in pictorial symbols (12)
13 Small and dainty (6)
15 Trinidad and ___ : country (6)
17 Ability to acquire and apply knowledge (12)
20 Capital of Vietnam (5)
21 Imaginary mischievous sprite (7)
22 Holding close (8)
23 ___ Blyton: writer (4)

Down

1 Pays homage to (8)
2 Out of fashion (5)
4 Seldom (6)
5 Having an acrid wit (5-7)
6 United States (7)
7 Hardens (4)
8 Not special (3-2-3-4)
12 Ruled with authority (8)
14 People who rent property (7)
16 Large container (6)
18 Synthetic fabric (5)
19 Keep away from (4)

No. 9

Across

1 Harbinger of spring; crazy (6)
7 Professional comedian (8)
8 Cut of pork (3)
9 Flat-bottomed rowing boat (6)
10 Small symbol or graphic (4)
11 Fortune-telling card (5)
13 Refiles (anag) (7)
15 Saw; noticed (7)
17 No longer fresh (of food) (5)
21 Scottish singer-songwriter (4)
22 Red salad fruit (6)
23 State of matter (3)
24 Written communications (8)
25 Representation of a concept; diagram (6)

Down

1 Roman military unit (6)
2 Arched shape of a road (6)
3 Proposal; suggestion (5)
4 Brought forth (7)
5 Writer of the words to a song (8)
6 Return on investment (6)
12 Effusion (8)
14 Savings for the future (4,3)
16 Stopped temporarily (6)
18 Climax or culmination (6)
19 ___ Cuthbert: Kim Bauer in 24 (6)
20 Accumulate (5)

No. 10

Across

1 Band whose frontman is Jarvis Cocker (4)
3 People who shape horseshoes (8)
9 These remove pencil marks (7)
10 Appear suddenly (3,2)
11 Climbing vine (3)
12 Possessor (5)
13 Produce as a fruit (5)
15 Principle of morality (5)
17 Main artery (5)
18 Sticky substance (3)
19 Gold block (5)
20 Violent troublemakers (7)
21 Plummet (8)
22 Extremely (4)

Down

1 Eg rain or snow (13)
2 Given to disclosing secrets (5)
4 Take as being true (6)
5 Duplication (12)
6 Erase or remove (7)
7 In a manner that exceeds what is necessary (13)
8 Feeling depressed (5-7)
14 Optical illusions (7)
16 History play by Shakespeare (5,1)
18 Large waterbirds (5)

13

No. 11

¹		²		■	³	⁴		⁵		⁶		⁷

(grid with numbered cells 1–23 as shown)

Across

1 True information (4)
3 Highly seasoned smoked beef (8)
9 Imaginary line around the earth (7)
10 Loft (5)
11 Striped animal (5)
12 Platform (7)
13 Person who fails to turn up (2-4)
15 Manage; hold (6)
17 Low protective wall (7)
18 Composition for a solo instrument (5)
20 Visual representation (5)
21 Coat; decorate lavishly (7)
22 Absurd representation of something (8)
23 Participate in a game (4)

Down

1 Temperature at which water turns to ice (8,5)
2 Tiny piece of food (5)
4 ___ borealis: Northern Lights (6)
5 Clearness (12)
6 Changed (7)
7 Ineptly (13)
8 Atmospheric layer (12)
14 Film directed by Stephen Gaghan (7)
16 Oxford ___ : famous London road (6)
19 Customary (5)

No. 12

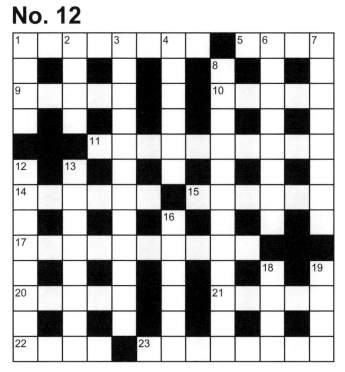

Across

1 Refuge (8)
5 ___ Khan: British boxer (4)
9 Estuary (5)
10 Drives out from a place (5)
11 Small community (10)
14 Inclined at an angle (6)
15 Abandon a plan (6)
17 Path of a projectile (10)
20 Representative (5)
21 Savour (5)
22 Fencing sword (4)
23 Interpret in a certain way (8)

Down

1 Dagger handle (4)
2 School bedroom (abbrev) (4)
3 Accomplishments (12)
4 Sad pot (anag) (6)
6 Extremely accomplished (8)
7 Flower-shaped competition awards (8)
8 Fellowship (12)
12 Apartment cohabitant (8)
13 Eg from Tokyo (8)
16 Room where an artist works (6)
18 Slightly open (4)
19 Sort (4)

No. 13

Across

1 Branch of physics (11)
9 Brightly coloured parrot (5)
10 Bleat of a sheep (3)
11 Play a guitar (5)
12 Giraffes have long ones (5)
13 Apparition (8)
16 Secondary personality (5,3)
18 Cuban folk dance (5)
21 Small and elegant (5)
22 Consume food (3)
23 ___ Rhymes: rapper (5)
24 Study of lawbreaking (11)

Down

2 Member of the band Blue (3,4)
3 Regular journey to and from work (7)
4 Alcove (6)
5 Certain to fail (2-3)
6 Having three dimensions (5)
7 Not held up (11)
8 Make in bulk (4-7)
14 Seven-a-side game (7)
15 Capital of China (7)
17 Make less tight (6)
19 Female parent (5)
20 Collection of songs (5)

No. 14

Across

1 Cameron ___ : actress (4)
3 Transport systems (8)
9 Feeling guilty (7)
10 Enumerates (5)
11 Perceptions (12)
14 ___ Thurman: Kill Bill actress (3)
16 Period of keeping awake to pray (5)
17 Dove sound (3)
18 Insistently (12)
21 Language of the Romans (5)
22 Garden flower (7)
23 Wood preserver (8)
24 Wire lattice (4)

Down

1 Conversation (8)
2 Remains of a fire (5)
4 Primary colour (3)
5 A large number (12)
6 Chemical element with atomic number 33 (7)
7 Mediocre (2-2)
8 Enhancements (12)
12 Anxiety (5)
13 Person of varied learning (8)
15 Disciple (7)
19 Sudden forward thrust (5)
20 Coalition of countries (4)
22 Tap (anag) (3)

No. 15

Across

1. ___ powder: bathroom item (6)
7. German shepherd dog (8)
8. Eg almond or pecan (3)
9. Archimedes' famous cry (6)
10. Not any of (4)
11. Short letters (5)
13. Film or play texts (7)
15. Halted (7)
17. Cairo is in this country (5)
21. Just and unbiased (4)
22. Marked by friendly companionship (6)
23. Bottle top (3)
24. Expression of gratitude (5,3)
25. Women who are about to marry (6)

Down

1. Connective tissue (6)
2. Most recent (6)
3. Labyrinths (5)
4. With an attitude of suspicion (7)
5. Impeding growth (8)
6. Large seabird (6)
12. Running out (8)
14. Jumpers (7)
16. Of inferior quality (6)
18. Shouted out very loudly (6)
19. Buys and sells goods (6)
20. Clean thoroughly (5)

No. 16

Across

1 Narrow sea inlets (6)
5 Cry (3)
7 Up to the time when (5)
8 Sculptured figures (7)
9 Fractional monetary unit (5)
10 Patrimony (8)
12 Shelter; place of refuge (6)
14 Expert in a particular subject (6)
17 Beetle larva that bores into timber (8)
18 Compact (5)
20 Coming from the south (7)
21 Maritime (5)
22 Hog (3)
23 Level a charge against (6)

Down

2 Extreme nervousness (7)
3 Uncertain (8)
4 Halt (4)
5 Angled; biased (7)
6 Look after an infant (7)
7 Customary practice (5)
11 Dead end (3-2-3)
12 Deliver by parachute (3-4)
13 Expressing boredom with the mouth (7)
15 Intrusions (7)
16 Regal (5)
19 Feeling of resentment or jealousy (4)

No. 17

Across

1 Answer to a problem (8)
5 ___ Yorke: Radiohead lead singer (4)
8 Country whose capital is Tripoli (5)
9 Mark the boundaries of (7)
10 Fractional part (7)
12 French bean (7)
14 Eg a resident of Rome (7)
16 Feared greatly (7)
18 Sheer dress fabric (7)
19 Device used to give support (5)
20 Spun thread used for knitting (4)
21 Climbed (8)

Down

1 Vend (4)
2 Clumsy person (6)
3 Rise above (9)
4 Strangest (6)
6 ___ pigeon: trained bird (6)
7 Random change (8)
11 Fragile (9)
12 Paper printout of data (4,4)
13 Mendicant (6)
14 Standards to be aimed at (6)
15 Towards the inside (6)
17 Action (4)

No. 18

Across

1	Celtic priest (5)
4	Not anything (7)
7	Less moist (5)
8	Relating to a topic (8)
9	Extravagant meal (5)
11	Made better (8)
15	At work (2-3-3)
17	Horse (anag) (5)
19	Harmful in effect (8)
20	Correct (5)
21	Tortilla rolled around a filling (7)
22	Detailed assessment of accounts (5)

Down

1	Regions (9)
2	Not tidy (7)
3	Deny any responsibility for (7)
4	Beginner (6)
5	Inspirational people (6)
6	Requirements (5)
10	Tempestuous (9)
12	Grotesque monster (7)
13	Expelled (7)
14	Bow and arrow expert (6)
16	Papal representative (6)
18	Japanese poem (5)

CROSSWORD

No. 19

Across

1 Group of actors in a show (4)
3 Not genuine (8)
9 Golfing measure of distance (7)
10 Pleasing view (5)
11 Metal container; element (3)
12 Fortunate (5)
13 Follows orders (5)
15 ___ Willis: daughter of Demi Moore (5)
17 Smell (5)
18 Performance by a musician (3)
19 Cage for small pets (5)
20 Insubstantial (7)
21 Send to a different place (8)
22 Soon; shortly (4)

Down

1 Code-breaker (13)
2 Warning noise from an emergency vehicle (5)
4 Satisfy (6)
5 Public official (5,7)
6 Bone in the ear (7)
7 Black Eyed Peas star (5,8)
8 Mapmaker (12)
14 Planned (7)
16 Adhesive putty (6)
18 Grumble (5)

No. 20

Across

1 Opposite of Northern (8)
5 Tibetan Buddhist monk (4)
8 Pertaining to the voice (5)
9 Flat highland (7)
10 Segmented worm (7)
12 Foolish person (informal) (4-3)
14 Distant settlement (7)
16 South American country (7)
18 Unlawful (7)
19 Large waterbird (5)
20 Expose to danger (4)
21 US state (8)

Down

1 Rescue (4)
2 Straighten out (6)
3 District of Los Angeles (9)
4 Do something again (6)
6 Ancient (3-3)
7 Artificial water channel (8)
11 Longing for something past (9)
12 Owner of an establishment providing lodgings (8)
13 Constructs (6)
14 Public speaker (6)
15 Pungent edible bulbs (6)
17 State of confusion; disorder (4)

CROSSWORD

No. 21

Across

1 Manure (4)
3 Small biting fly (8)
9 Sporting dog (7)
10 Pick out; choose (5)
11 Surrender (12)
14 Beer (3)
16 Ballroom dance (5)
17 Secret retreat (3)
18 Extremely large (12)
21 Sculptured symbol (5)
22 Ornamental screen (7)
23 Reassign (8)
24 Push; poke (4)

Down

1 Eg a trumpeter or pianist (8)
2 Muscular contraction (5)
4 Nocturnal bird of prey (3)
5 The ? symbol (8,4)
6 Freezing (3-4)
7 Solemn promise (4)
8 Absolute authority in any sphere (12)
12 Cloth woven from flax (5)
13 Examined in detail (8)
15 Trialled or tested (7)
19 Alcoholic drink made from apples (5)
20 Jelly or culture medium (4)
22 17th Greek letter (3)

No. 22

Across

1	Entirety (8)
5	Imitated (4)
8	Poisonous (5)
9	Get back (7)
10	Empty (7)
12	Laugh (7)
14	Severe (7)
16	Underwater projectile (7)
18	Nerve impulses (7)
19	Journeys (5)
20	Wise man; herb (4)
21	Visitors to a place (8)

Down

1	Catherine ___ : British comedienne (4)
2	Dinner jacket (6)
3	Profitable (9)
4	Flourish (6)
6	Keyboard instruments (6)
7	Relating to the home (8)
11	Electrical component (9)
12	Competitions (8)
13	Eg using a towel (6)
14	Gaming tile (6)
15	Belonging to them (6)
17	Sues (anag) (4)

No. 23

Across

1 Frivolous (5-6)
9 Venomous snake (5)
10 Excessively (3)
11 Fish basket (5)
12 Pertaining to sound (5)
13 Person with an appreciation of beauty (8)
16 Cooking measure (8)
18 Frozen fruit juice on a stick (5)
21 Diacritical mark (5)
22 A man; fellow (3)
23 Civilian dress (5)
24 Double entendre (4,2,5)

Down

2 Ardent (7)
3 In good physical condition (7)
4 Relatively limited (of an amount) (6)
5 Conventions (5)
6 ___ John: Rocket Man singer (5)
7 Study of human history (11)
8 Act of hiding something (11)
14 Type of porch (7)
15 Get rid of something (7)
17 Seabird (6)
19 Faithful (5)
20 Delicious (5)

No. 24

Across

1 Always in a similar role (of an actor) (8)
5 Arduous journey (4)
9 Element with atomic number 5 (5)
10 Indian monetary unit (5)
11 Features; attributes (10)
14 Groups of three (6)
15 Parrot sound (6)
17 Antibiotic (10)
20 Aromatic spice (5)
21 Relation by marriage (2-3)
22 Stringed instrument (4)
23 Substance that causes a reaction (8)

Down

1 Hollow pipe (4)
2 South American country (4)
3 Showed not to be true (12)
4 Excessively casual (6)
6 Act of retaliation (8)
7 Memento (8)
8 Precondition (12)
12 Not usual (8)
13 Roadside board showing directions (8)
16 Worldwide (6)
18 Shoe with a wooden sole (4)
19 Link a town with another (4)

No. 25

Across

1 After the beginning of (4)
3 Type of state (8)
9 Witty saying (7)
10 Looking tired (5)
11 Money container (5)
12 Tell a story (7)
13 Live in (6)
15 Distinctive mode of pronunciation (6)
17 Meriting (7)
18 Adult insect (5)
20 Thin pancake (5)
21 Do away with a need (7)
22 Catastrophe (8)
23 Openly refuse to obey an order (4)

Down

1 Wet behind the ears (13)
2 One who always puts in a lot of effort (5)
4 Fur of a stoat (6)
5 Perform below expectation (12)
6 Discharge from a hole in a pipe (7)
7 Sweets (13)
8 Amiability (12)
14 Thoroughfares (7)
16 Refuse to acknowledge (6)
19 Humiliate (5)

28

No. 26

Across

1 Defeated (8)
5 Boyfriend or male admirer (4)
8 Turf out (5)
9 Ring or echo (7)
10 Having a resemblance to another item (7)
12 Things done (7)
14 Eg anger or love (7)
16 Fish-eating birds of prey (7)
18 Make a study of (7)
19 Stand up (5)
20 ___ Berra: baseball player (4)
21 Edible snail (8)

Down

1 Still to be paid (4)
2 Evoke (6)
3 Complete list of items (9)
4 Bog; confused situation (6)
6 Matches (6)
7 Support (8)
11 Sensational dramatic work (9)
12 Organised activism (8)
13 Jumped up (6)
14 Steers (anag) (6)
15 Doing nothing (6)
17 Undergarment (4)

No. 27

Across

1 Unwillingness to accept the views of others (11)
9 Opposite of thin (5)
10 Illumination unit (3)
11 Water lily (5)
12 Benefactor (5)
13 Small pincers (8)
16 Progresses (8)
18 Golf clubs (5)
21 Section of a long poem (5)
22 Type of vase (3)
23 Prohibited by social custom (5)
24 Trustworthy (11)

Down

2 Therein (anag) (7)
3 Unusually large (7)
4 Magical potion (6)
5 Raised a question (5)
6 Large intestine (5)
7 Harmful (11)
8 Sayings (11)
14 Guglielmo ___ : radio pioneer (7)
15 Thing causing outrage (7)
17 Seaport in South Africa (6)
19 Snow leopard (5)
20 Scheme intended to deceive (3-2)

No. 28

Across

1 Poker stake (4)
3 Cherish; preserve (8)
9 Community of nuns (7)
10 Unabridged (5)
11 Spoil (3)
12 Andrew Lloyd Webber musical (5)
13 Streamlined (5)
15 Move sideways (5)
17 Individual things (5)
18 Snow runner (3)
19 Display freely (5)
20 The small details of something (7)
21 A formal exposition (8)
22 Make a request to God (4)

Down

1 Supporting musical part (13)
2 Radio receiver (5)
4 Stinging weed (6)
5 The management of a home (12)
6 Slope (7)
7 Noteworthy and rare (13)
8 Re-evaluation (12)
14 Expect; suppose to be true (7)
16 True skin (6)
18 Indian lute (5)

No. 29

1		2		■	3	4		5		6		7

Across

1 Hollow in a cliff (4)
3 Person who supports a cause (8)
9 Large wine bottles (7)
10 Device that splits light (5)
11 Concerning (5)
12 Repair a vehicle (7)
13 Smiles contemptuously (6)
15 ___ Holden: English actress (6)
17 Sharp no (anag) (7)
18 Courage; boldness (5)
20 Severe (5)
21 Form of speech specific to a region (7)
22 Fairness (8)
23 Raised area of skin; swollen mark (4)

Down

1 Sympathetic and merciful (13)
2 ___ Mortensen: actor (5)
4 Discontinuance; neglect (6)
5 Based on untested ideas (12)
6 Omission of a sound when speaking (7)
7 Unpredictable (13)
8 Underground (12)
14 Choose and follow (7)
16 Incidental remarks (6)
19 Pass a rope through (5)

No. 30

Across

- **1** Engrossing (8)
- **5** Confine; snare (4)
- **8** Faint southern constellation (5)
- **9** Recipient of funding (7)
- **10** Food pantries (7)
- **12** Spread through (7)
- **14** Alongside each other (7)
- **16** Sideways looks (7)
- **18** More fortunate (7)
- **19** Recently made (5)
- **20** Close by (4)
- **21** Unit of pronunciation (8)

Down

- **1** Raised edges (4)
- **2** Thin decorative coating (6)
- **3** Emotionally disturbing (9)
- **4** Small worry; irritate (6)
- **6** More precisely (6)
- **7** Agreeable (8)
- **11** Remorseful (9)
- **12** Scaly anteater (8)
- **13** Instrument panel (6)
- **14** Far from the target (6)
- **15** Word that qualifies another (6)
- **17** Item of footwear (4)

No. 31

Across

1 Aim to achieve something (6)
5 Gratuity (3)
7 Jessica ___-Hill : British heptathlete (5)
8 Ionised gases (7)
9 Acoustic detection system (5)
10 Observer (8)
12 Cruel ruler (6)
14 Russian carriage (6)
17 ___ Cruz: Spanish actress (8)
18 Discharge (5)
20 Object used in the kitchen (7)
21 Red cosmetic powder (5)
22 State (3)
23 Allocate a duty (6)

Down

2 White and lustrous (hair) (7)
3 Making a deep resonant sound (8)
4 Small social insects (4)
5 Huge wave (7)
6 Powdered spice (7)
7 Town in Surrey; sheer (anag) (5)
11 Household cooling devices (8)
12 Skills (7)
13 Lively festivities (7)
15 Rudyard ___ : novelist (7)
16 Variety show (5)
19 Solicit custom (4)

No. 32

Across

1 Place where fighting occurs (11)
9 ___ Way: famous Roman road (5)
10 Make a mistake (3)
11 Feign (5)
12 Long pointed elephant teeth (5)
13 Orchestral piece at the beginning of an opera (8)
16 Without shoes (8)
18 Strange and mysterious (5)
21 Speak without preparation (2-3)
22 Organ of sight (3)
23 Arm of a body of water (5)
24 Inevitably (11)

Down

2 Charged with a crime (7)
3 Crisp plain fabric (7)
4 Simpler (6)
5 Clumsy (5)
6 City in West Yorkshire (5)
7 Needleworker (11)
8 Fit to be seen (11)
14 Treason (anag) (7)
15 Expressing deep feeling (7)
17 Mixes up or confuses (6)
19 ___ Witherspoon: actress (5)
20 Select class (5)

CROSSWORD

No. 33

Across

1 Animal feet (4)
3 Etiquette (8)
9 Jealous (7)
10 Short treatise (5)
11 Blade for rowing a boat (3)
12 Name applied to something (5)
13 Corpulent (5)
15 A Fish Called ___ : film (5)
17 Position carefully (5)
18 Polite address for a man (3)
19 Pastoral poem (5)
20 ___ Joan Hart: American actress (7)
21 Kernel's hard surrounding (8)
22 Saw; observed (4)

Down

1 Presupposition (13)
2 Vacillate (5)
4 Leaser (anag) (6)
5 Casual chatter (6-6)
6 Large room (7)
7 The ___ / ___ : Fairy tale by Hans Christian Andersen (6,7)
8 A grouping of states (12)
14 Someone who studies data (7)
16 Standard; usual (6)
18 Impudent; full of spirit (5)

No. 34

Across

1 Front of a building (6)
5 Appropriate (3)
7 Chubby (5)
8 Reaches a destination (7)
9 Angered; irritated (5)
10 Timetable (8)
12 Chant; speak solemnly (6)
14 Large strong boxes (6)
17 Searching for prey (8)
18 Strong cords (5)
20 Leguminous plant also called lucerne (7)
21 Tarnish (5)
22 Newt (3)
23 Functional (6)

Down

2 Eg from Ethiopia (7)
3 Money paid to shareholders (8)
4 Whirring sound (4)
5 Is relevant (7)
6 Dealers (7)
7 Lyrical poem or song (5)
11 Exhibitionists (4-4)
12 Do repeatedly (7)
13 Storm (7)
15 Containerful (7)
16 Ordered arrangement (5)
19 Performance by one actor (4)

CROSSWORD

No. 35

Across

1 Manage (4)
3 Disdainful rejection (5-3)
9 Perfect happiness (7)
10 Teacher (5)
11 Arrive at (5)
12 Grassy clump (7)
13 Measure of loudness (6)
15 Coiffure (6)
17 Without interruption (3-4)
18 Absorbent cloth (5)
20 ___ Hayes: US singer (5)
21 Obtained from a source (7)
22 Unnecessary (8)
23 Small island (4)

Down

1 Violation (13)
2 Weatherproof coat (5)
4 Cooks in the oven (6)
5 Adequate (12)
6 Located in the fresh air (7)
7 Prescience (13)
8 Relating to numbers (12)
14 Ancestry (7)
16 Shovels (6)
19 Married women (5)

No. 36

Across

1 Female servant (4)
3 Coming into view (8)
9 Subatomic particles such as electrons (7)
10 Pale brownish-yellow colour (5)
11 Mountain pass (3)
12 Lubricated (5)
13 Walked at a steady speed (5)
15 Eg heart or liver (5)
17 Sailing boat (5)
18 Pouch; enclosed space (3)
19 Go inside (5)
20 Washing sponges (7)
21 Splashing with water (8)
22 ___-Jacques Rousseau: philosopher (4)

Down

1 Spite (13)
2 Drive forward (5)
4 Picture produced from many small pieces (6)
5 Evergreen shrub (12)
6 Item used by asthma sufferers (7)
7 British actress who became an MP (6,7)
8 Repository for misplaced items (4,8)
14 Not as tall (7)
16 Unit of volume (6)
18 Raised floor or platform (5)

39

No. 37

Across

1 Medieval musician (8)
5 Clutched (4)
8 Talent; ability (5)
9 Night lights (7)
10 ___ lettuce: salad vegetable (7)
12 ___ ball: item used by clairvoyants (7)
14 Not varying (7)
16 Moved off course (7)
18 Yearbook (7)
19 Nimble (5)
20 Short letter (4)
21 Starlike symbol (8)

Down

1 Vex (4)
2 Tidily (6)
3 Region (9)
4 Have as a consequence (6)
6 Sound reflections (6)
7 Have a different opinion (8)
11 Vindicate (9)
12 One who steers a boat (8)
13 On time (6)
14 Proclamations (6)
15 Swimming costume (6)
17 Welsh emblem (4)

No. 38

Across

1 ___ Barlow: actress (6)
7 Assists; holds up (8)
8 ___ Carter: snooker player (3)
9 Small summerhouse (6)
10 Extreme anger (4)
11 Eating plans (5)
13 Disease (anag) (7)
15 Got on a ship (7)
17 Important topic (5)
21 Average value (4)
22 Slender; thin (6)
23 Title of a married woman (3)
24 Truly (8)
25 Inn (6)

Down

1 Followed a route or signal (6)
2 A political exile (6)
3 Twisted to one side (5)
4 Argues against (7)
5 Befuddles (8)
6 Gazed (6)
12 Sharpness (of taste) (8)
14 Mental strain (7)
16 Medium-sized feline (6)
18 Obstruct (6)
19 Thomas ___ : US inventor (6)
20 Period of darkness (5)

CROSSWORD

No. 39

Across

1 Having four right angles (of a shape) (11)
9 Gate fastener (5)
10 Criticise strongly (3)
11 Salivate (5)
12 Poetic verse (5)
13 Terminated (8)
16 In spite of the fact (8)
18 Judged (5)
21 Franz ___ : Hungarian composer (5)
22 Louse egg (3)
23 Floor of a building (5)
24 Devices popular before computers existed (11)

Down

2 Explain in detail (7)
3 Greatest in height (7)
4 Basic character of something (6)
5 Wedding official (5)
6 Put into use (5)
7 Unconcerned (11)
8 Drug causing a loss of sensation (11)
14 Small onion-like bulb (7)
15 Chaser (7)
17 Reveal (anag) (6)
19 Tawdry (5)
20 Research deeply (5)

No. 40

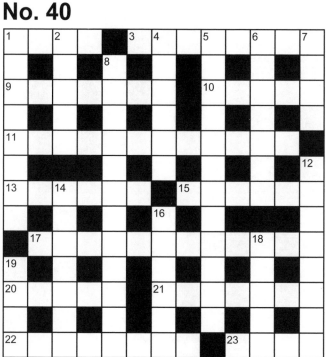

Across

1	Having pains (4)
3	Corrosive precipitation (4,4)
9	Daydream (7)
10	Scorch (5)
11	Contradictory (12)
13	Old Portuguese currency (6)
15	Multiples of twenty (6)
17	Impossible to achieve (12)
20	Change (5)
21	Japanese dish of raw fish (7)
22	Wave or flourish a weapon (8)
23	Narrate (4)

Down

1	Flight carriers (8)
2	Total disorder (5)
4	Title of Roman emperors (6)
5	Clarity (12)
6	Shaped like a ring (7)
7	Negative votes (4)
8	Planned in advance (12)
12	Exceptional (8)
14	Musical composition (7)
16	US state with capital Topeka (6)
18	Sandy fawn colour (5)
19	Sharp bristle (4)

CROSSWORD

No. 41

Across

1 11th Greek letter (6)
5 Recede (3)
7 Borough of New York City (5)
8 Study of the body (7)
9 General hatred (5)
10 Freed from an obligation (8)
12 Land surrounded by water (6)
14 Each (6)
17 Longing (8)
18 Annelid worm with suckers (5)
20 French city (7)
21 God (5)
22 Expected at a certain time (3)
23 Set fire to (6)

Down

2 Incorporates into (7)
3 Letting go of (8)
4 Spool-like toy (2-2)
5 Make amends (7)
6 Blackberry bush (7)
7 Computer memory units (5)
11 In a fair manner (8)
12 Country whose capital is Reykjavik (7)
13 Citrus drink (7)
15 Twist out of shape (7)
16 Decomposition (5)
19 Person who will inherit (4)

No. 42

Across

1 Noble gas (5)
4 Large flat dish (7)
7 Uniform jacket (5)
8 No longer in fashion (8)
9 Desire to hurt someone (5)
11 Concurring (8)
15 Intended to teach (8)
17 Chris ___ : tennis champion (5)
19 Piece of printed matter (8)
20 Colossus (5)
21 One who assesses metals (7)
22 Military blockade (5)

Down

1 Source of irritation (9)
2 Stringed instruments (7)
3 Contradicted; made ineffective (7)
4 Clay ___ : shooting target (6)
5 Hits hard (6)
6 Be alive; be real (5)
10 Senior manager (9)
12 Military gestures (7)
13 Tall tower (7)
14 Fleet of ships (6)
16 Line of equal pressure on a map (6)
18 Concealing garments (5)

No. 43

Across

1 Current of air (4)
3 Section of a train (8)
9 Assistant (7)
10 Trims (5)
11 Shape of something (12)
14 Periodic publication (abbrev) (3)
16 Vital organ (5)
17 Anger (3)
18 US state (12)
21 Smarter (5)
22 Dearly cherished (7)
23 Negotiator (8)
24 Lids (anag) (4)

Down

1 Eye condition (8)
2 Exhibited (5)
4 Mature (3)
5 Monotonously (12)
6 Relating to knowledge based on deduction (1,6)
7 Otherwise (4)
8 Abnormal anxiety about health (12)
12 Fleshy (5)
13 Took into account (8)
15 Made a conjecture about (7)
19 A central point (5)
20 Moved through water (4)
22 Cry of disapproval (3)

No. 44

Across

1   Type of motor cycle (5)
4   Short story (7)
7   Cathedral (5)
8   Scruffily (8)
9   Store in a secret place (5)
11   Exclamation of joy (8)
15   The scholastic world (8)
17   Push gently (5)
19   Courgette (US) (8)
20   Confusion (3-2)
21   Determined (7)
22   Seven (anag) (5)

Down

1   Deformed (9)
2   Due (7)
3   Fall slowly (of a liquid) (7)
4   Central parts of cells (6)
5   Liken to; correspond (6)
6   Unshapely masses; swellings (5)
10   Extremely funny (9)
12   Instruct (7)
13   Encroach (7)
14   Long-legged rodent (6)
16   Brought about (6)
18   Join together (5)

No. 45

Across

1 Understate (8)
5 Move in water (4)
9 Imitative of the past (5)
10 Ahead of time (5)
11 Person conducting a sale of lots (10)
14 Place of worship (6)
15 Topics for debate (6)
17 Lift secrecy restrictions on (10)
20 Agreeable sound or tune (5)
21 Meal (5)
22 Wine container (4)
23 Naive or sentimental (4-4)

Down

1 Dreadful (4)
2 James ___ : Scottish engineer (4)
3 Bump (12)
4 Doles out (6)
6 Excessively emotional (6,2)
7 Female head of a borough (8)
8 Regretfully (12)
12 Pertaining to education (8)
13 Political meetings (8)
16 The spirit or soul (6)
18 Solely (4)
19 Country bordered by Libya and Sudan (4)

No. 46

Across

1 Friends (4)
3 Person in second place (6-2)
9 Form of retaliation (7)
10 Awake from slumber (5)
11 Alphabetical list in a book (5)
12 Aseptic (7)
13 Given out (6)
15 Young swan (6)
17 Modified (7)
18 Greeting (5)
20 Lazed (5)
21 People in jail (7)
22 Recently married (5-3)
23 Military force (4)

Down

1 Involvement (13)
2 Cherished (5)
4 Anxious (6)
5 Short tale told to children (7,5)
6 Gathering of old friends (7)
7 Affectedly (13)
8 By chance (12)
14 Lacking depth (7)
16 Suggestion (6)
19 Coming after (5)

CROSSWORD

No. 47

Across

1 Piece of evidence (4)
3 Places where fruit trees are grown (8)
9 Removes impurities (7)
10 Holy chalice (5)
11 Cereal plant (3)
12 Piece of bread (5)
13 Repeat something once more (5)
15 Keen (5)
17 Consumer (5)
18 Mock (3)
19 Many times (5)
20 Necessary (7)
21 Anxious uncertainty (8)
22 Soft cheese (4)

Down

1 Period of the Palaeozoic era (13)
2 Unsuitable (5)
4 Simple; unrefined (6)
5 Joyously unrestrained (4-8)
6 Raising (7)
7 25th anniversary celebration (6,7)
8 Disturbance; act of meddling (12)
14 Large areas of land (7)
16 Organs that secrete (6)
18 Send someone to a medical specialist (5)

No. 48

CROSSWORD

Across

1 With hands on the hips (6)
5 Chatter (3)
7 Crumble (5)
8 Bright red (7)
9 Network points where lines intersect (5)
10 Separated (8)
12 Ice homes (6)
14 Dried grape (6)
17 Measure of the heat content of a system (8)
18 Arm joint (5)
20 Giggles (7)
21 Leaves out (5)
22 Tree that bears acorns (3)
23 Snarls (6)

Down

2 Striking with the foot (7)
3 Dancing hall (8)
4 In the not too distant future (4)
5 Eg male and female (7)
6 Cricket hitters (7)
7 Flammable liquid used as an anaesthetic (5)
11 Pitiful (8)
12 Raging fire (7)
13 Captain's record (7)
15 Endanger (7)
16 Individual things (5)
19 Wire (anag) (4)

No. 49

Across

1 Lump or blob (6)
7 Cartoon artist (8)
8 Pub (3)
9 ___ Baker: Bucks Fizz member (6)
10 ___ Stewart: ex-England cricketer (4)
11 Abominable snowmen (5)
13 Reunites (7)
15 Coatings (7)
17 Yearned for (5)
21 Girl's toy (4)
22 Disallow; prevent (6)
23 Ground condensation (3)
24 Light from our star (8)
25 Totter or tremble (6)

Down

1 Of delicate beauty (6)
2 Surgical knife (6)
3 Sets of two things (5)
4 Telephoned (7)
5 Type of pasta (8)
6 Mirthless (6)
12 Utopian (8)
14 Movement of vehicles en masse (7)
16 Exit; Bible book (6)
18 Inclined one's head to show approval (6)
19 Storage compartment (6)
20 Advised; encouraged (5)

No. 50

Across

1 Droops (4)
3 Highly critical remark (8)
9 Give too much money (7)
10 Positions in a hierarchy (5)
11 An idea that is added later (12)
14 Possesses (3)
16 Show indifference with the shoulders (5)
17 Flightless bird (3)
18 Laudatory (12)
21 Recurrent topic (5)
22 Gun holder (7)
23 Social insect (8)
24 Fundraising party (4)

Down

1 Puts up with (8)
2 The ___ Gatsby: F. Scott Fitzgerald novel (5)
4 Beam of light (3)
5 Brusque and surly (12)
6 Female spirit (7)
7 Long pointed tooth (4)
8 Brutally; harshly (12)
12 Equine animal (5)
13 Exempt from tax (4-4)
15 Operating doctor (7)
19 Name of a book (5)
20 Skin irritation (4)
22 Weeding tool (3)

No. 51

Across

1 Andre ___ : former US tennis player (6)
7 Private detective (8)
8 ___ Titmuss: TV personality (3)
9 Take into custody (6)
10 Young children (4)
11 Most respected person in a field (5)
13 Share; portion (7)
15 A child beginning to walk (7)
17 Aqualung (5)
21 Ale (4)
22 Containerful (6)
23 Sphere or globe (3)
24 Adolescent (8)
25 Sour to the taste (6)

Down

1 Became less intense (6)
2 Bird enclosure (6)
3 Small piece of land (5)
4 Tenured (anag) (7)
5 Free from sensual desire (8)
6 Put an end to (6)
12 Abiding; lasting (8)
14 Green vegetation (7)
16 Complied with a command (6)
18 Remove goods from a van (6)
19 Middle Eastern language (6)
20 Additional; excess (5)

No. 52

Across

1 Close associate (8)
5 Exchange (4)
8 ___ del Sol: region of Spain (5)
9 Remains (7)
10 Strangeness (7)
12 Large marine flatfish (7)
14 Most important (7)
16 Acquire as an heir (7)
18 Diplomatic building (7)
19 Island in the Mediterranean Sea (5)
20 Utters (4)
21 Device recording distance travelled (8)

Down

1 Of like kind (4)
2 Banish; eliminate (6)
3 Tailless Australian marsupial (5,4)
4 Orange vegetable (6)
6 Jams tight (6)
7 Gratification (8)
11 Exercise of absolute power (9)
12 Sanctity (8)
13 Round and plump (6)
14 Remained in a certain place (6)
15 Procure; sign up (6)
17 Bristle (4)

CROSSWORD

No. 53

Across

1 Going on and on (5-6)
9 Economise (5)
10 ___ chart: type of graph (3)
11 Service colour of the army (5)
12 Divide in two (5)
13 Eastern (8)
16 Country in NE Africa (8)
18 George ___ : Middlemarch writer (5)
21 ___ Klum: supermodel (5)
22 Come together (3)
23 Island in the Bay of Naples (5)
24 Happiness (11)

Down

2 Unpredictable (7)
3 Military flags (7)
4 ___ Fox: English actress (6)
5 Extent (5)
6 Country in the Himalayas (5)
7 Admit to be true (11)
8 Joyful occasion (11)
14 Soft and reactive metallic element (7)
15 20th letter of the Greek alphabet (7)
17 Dick ___ : English highwayman (6)
19 Snow home (5)
20 Implied without being stated (5)

No. 54

Across

1	Proverbs (4)
3	Accommodating (8)
9	Comparison (7)
10	Gives as a reference (5)
11	Conflict of opinion (12)
14	Intentionally so written (3)
16	Colour lightly (5)
17	Dr ___ : US record producer (3)
18	Indifferent to (12)
21	Seemingly (combining form) (5)
22	Musical composition (7)
23	Annul or abolish (8)
24	Matured (4)

Down

1	A magical quality (8)
2	Erodes (5)
4	Purchase (3)
5	Ineptness (12)
6	Chanted (7)
7	Core meaning (4)
8	Having existed for a considerable time (4-8)
12	___ Els: golfer (5)
13	Promontory (8)
15	Mythical being (7)
19	Strong ringing sound (5)
20	Greenish-blue colour (4)
22	Very small child (3)

No. 55

Across

1 Individual properties (8)
5 Insincere moral talk; bank (4)
8 Titles (5)
9 Artistic movement (3,4)
10 Mocking (7)
12 Bivalve molluscs (7)
14 Spouts (7)
16 Silly talk (7)
18 Snobbish (7)
19 Sound made by a pig (5)
20 Holier than ___ : phrase (4)
21 Freshwater crustacean (8)

Down

1 Having a liking for (4)
2 Military forces (6)
3 Loosened by twisting (9)
4 Plays out (6)
6 Pertaining to vinegar (6)
7 Ideas (8)
11 Incredibly (9)
12 Salve (8)
13 Coarse cloth (6)
14 Sugary flower secretion (6)
15 Lapis ___ : blue gemstone (6)
17 Engrave; carve (4)

No. 56

Across

1 Reverse (4)
3 Lays in wait for (8)
9 Canvas shelters (7)
10 Relating to sound (5)
11 Stimulus (3)
12 Browned bread (5)
13 Edward ___ : composer (5)
15 Ancient object (5)
17 Social division in some societies (5)
18 Sense of self-esteem (3)
19 Move out of the way (5)
20 Inns (7)
21 Skilfully (8)
22 Dairy product (4)

Down

1 Inexplicable (13)
2 Move to music (5)
4 Pondering (6)
5 Ugly (12)
6 Pipe from which water can be drawn (7)
7 Impulsively (13)
8 Someone who sets up their own business (12)
14 Form or accumulate steadily (5-2)
16 Horizontal supporting beam (6)
18 Our planet (5)

No. 57

Across

1 Act of publishing in several places (11)
9 Remnant of a dying fire (5)
10 Cooling tool (3)
11 Of definite shape (5)
12 Dole out (5)
13 Stayed longer than necessary (8)
16 Imposing (8)
18 Mark or wear thin (5)
21 Spore-producing organisms (5)
22 Crux of a matter (3)
23 ___ Lewis: British singer (5)
24 Certainly (11)

Down

2 Screaming (7)
3 Cleared the bottom of a river (7)
4 Small round stone (6)
5 ___ firma: dry land (5)
6 Bits of meat of low value (5)
7 Annoying (11)
8 Direction (11)
14 Foliage (7)
15 Template (7)
17 Soak up (6)
19 Relating to a city (5)
20 Leaf of parchment (5)

No. 58

Across

1	Badger's home (4)
3	Shrill (8)
9	Visual symbolism (7)
10	Film (5)
11	Deceitfully (12)
14	Annoy constantly (3)
16	Complete; absolute (5)
17	Depression (3)
18	Discreditable (12)
21	Type of coffee drink (5)
22	Rowdy (7)
23	Capital of Jamaica (8)
24	Singe; burn (4)

Down

1	Breathing in sharply (8)
2	Jewelled headdress (5)
4	Very cold; slippery (3)
5	Money paid for work (12)
6	Not legally recognised; void (7)
7	Increased in size (4)
8	Main premises of a company (12)
12	Abatement (5)
13	Peacemaker (8)
15	Sparkle (7)
19	Type of soup (5)
20	Anti-aircraft fire (4)
22	___ Ferdinand: footballer (3)

No. 59

Across

1 Moves up and down on water (4)
3 Beneficial (8)
9 Most slothful (7)
10 Mournful song (5)
11 Someone skilled in penmanship (12)
13 Easily remembered (6)
15 Arch of the foot (6)
17 Narcissism (4-8)
20 Of the nose (5)
21 Have as a part (7)
22 Irritating (8)
23 Deciduous trees (4)

Down

1 Device that regulates water flow (8)
2 Grooved ring (5)
4 Go back (6)
5 Freedom from control (12)
6 Penalty (7)
7 In ___ : instead (4)
8 Charmingly (12)
12 Totally clean (8)
14 Senator (anag) (7)
16 Eg from New Delhi (6)
18 Be the same as (5)
19 Black ___ : Colombian bird (4)

No. 60

Across

1 Fence formed by bushes (8)
5 Musical composition (4)
9 Work hard (5)
10 Gave up power (5)
11 Directly; in person (4,2,4)
14 Margin of safety (6)
15 Plant of the dock family (6)
17 Government official (10)
20 Administrative capital of Bolivia (2,3)
21 Epic poem ascribed to Homer (5)
22 Repetition to aid memory (4)
23 Cheerily (8)

Down

1 Opposite of low (4)
2 Having two parts (4)
3 Lavish event (12)
4 States as one's opinion (6)
6 Chiropody (8)
7 Abruptly (8)
8 Sensory system used by dolphins (12)
12 Spherical (8)
13 Dilapidated (8)
16 Leguminous tree (6)
18 Flightless bird (4)
19 Indolently (4)

CROSSWORD

No. 61

Across

1 Chances of winning (4)
3 Makers (8)
9 Symbolic objects (7)
10 On two occasions (5)
11 Rigid (5)
12 Voted in to office (7)
13 Collections of photos (6)
15 Sporting venues (6)
17 Fifth Greek letter (7)
18 ___ Eastwood: US actor (5)
20 Enlighten (5)
21 Group of assistants (7)
22 Unable to appreciate music (4-4)
23 High-value playing cards (4)

Down

1 Exaggeration (13)
2 One of the United Arab Emirates (5)
4 Duster (anag) (6)
5 Establish as genuine (12)
6 Left out (7)
7 Loyalty in the face of trouble (13)
8 Working for oneself (4-8)
14 Stronghold (7)
16 ___ Bocelli: Italian operatic singer (6)
19 Type of chemical bond (5)

No. 62

Across

1	Squirt (6)
5	Home for a pig (3)
7	Distinguishing characteristic (5)
8	Persuasive relevance (7)
9	Happen again (5)
10	Beaten (8)
12	Pilfers (6)
14	Leapt in the air (6)
17	Disease-producing agent (8)
18	Loud metallic sound (5)
20	Cues given to performers (7)
21	Deserves (5)
22	Auction offer (3)
23	Measure of electrical current (6)

Down

2	Keep safe from harm (7)
3	Feeler (8)
4	Couple (4)
5	Overly conceited and arrogant (5-2)
6	Longed for (7)
7	Uses a keyboard (5)
11	Increase rapidly (8)
12	Yield (7)
13	Pledged to marry (7)
15	Voter (7)
16	Curbs; muffles (5)
19	___ Barlow: Take That singer (4)

No. 63

Across

1 Stifle (anag) (6)
4 Long essay or dissertation (6)
9 Defensive position in football (7)
10 A number defining position (7)
11 Burn (5)
12 Not heavy (5)
14 Nearby (5)
15 Male bee (5)
17 Mexican plant fibre (5)
18 Took along (7)
20 Made bare (7)
21 Spreads out and apart (6)
22 Very cold (6)

Down

1 Take a firm stand (6)
2 Plot outline for a play (8)
3 Oily organic compound (5)
5 Large bag (7)
6 Revolve (4)
7 Create by carving (6)
8 Company that transmits TV shows (11)
13 Greedy (8)
14 Very long (7)
15 Suspends; prevents (6)
16 Dodged (6)
17 Fantastic (5)
19 By word of mouth (4)

No. 64

Across

1	Body of running water (6)
5	Belgian town (3)
7	Explode (5)
8	Snared (7)
9	Herb (5)
10	Faithfulness (8)
12	Closely woven fabric (6)
14	___ jumping: extreme sport (6)
17	Lookout (8)
18	Simple song (5)
20	Type of treatment for a disorder (7)
21	Receive a ball in one's hands (5)
22	Bind (3)
23	Weigh up (6)

Down

2	Earthenware container (7)
3	Horrified (8)
4	Search for (4)
5	Remaining (7)
6	Unfavourable (7)
7	Amends (5)
11	Fairness (8)
12	Judgement (7)
13	Framework (7)
15	Frees from an obligation (7)
16	Sandy wasteland (5)
19	Abominable snowman (4)

CROSSWORD

No. 65

Across

1 Views about something (8)
5 Long narrative poem (4)
8 Fruit (5)
9 Eg swords and guns (7)
10 Japanese massage technique (7)
12 Live together (7)
14 Mournful poems (7)
16 Edges (7)
18 Kind of breakfast cereal (7)
19 All (5)
20 Cloth worn around the waist (4)
21 Discard (8)

Down

1 Gemstone (4)
2 Hinder (6)
3 Intoxicate (9)
4 Freshest (6)
6 Quickly (6)
7 Outfits (8)
11 Recent tip (anag) (9)
12 Vegetables (8)
13 Church instruments (6)
14 Large property with land; holding (6)
15 Urges to act (6)
17 ___ Giggs: football star (4)

No. 66

Across

1	Irritable (6)
4	Eclipsed (6)
9	Boastful behaviour (7)
10	Distance travelled (7)
11	Piece of writing (5)
12	Possessed (5)
14	Go stealthily or furtively (5)
15	Moth-___ : damaged (5)
17	Picture border (5)
18	Light compositions (7)
20	Type of optician (7)
21	Sewing instrument (6)
22	Lead batsman for a team (6)

Down

1	Pieces of furniture (6)
2	Send a signal (8)
3	Of great weight (5)
5	One's mental attitude (7)
6	Insect stage (4)
7	Be contingent upon (6)
8	Sponsor mice (anag) (11)
13	Symbols representing musical notes (8)
14	Breathing aid in water (7)
15	Banner or flag (6)
16	Clown (6)
17	Fall heavily (5)
19	This place (4)

No. 67

Across

1 Pulls at (4)
3 Loss of hearing (8)
9 Form of an element (7)
10 Small room used as a steam bath (5)
11 Threshold (5)
12 Analyse (7)
13 Liam ___ : Irish actor (6)
15 Stick to (6)
17 Tympanic membrane (7)
18 These protect you from rain (5)
20 Lift up (5)
21 Make better (7)
22 Containing less oxygen than usual (of air) (8)
23 Lyric poems (4)

Down

1 Simple problem-solving method (5,3,5)
2 Marrying man (5)
4 Number in a football team (6)
5 Popular takeaway food (4,3,5)
6 Learned (7)
7 Brazenness (13)
8 DIY stands for this (2-2-8)
14 Prior (7)
16 Extensive domain (6)
19 Egg-shaped solid (5)

No. 68

Across

1 Breakfast food (6)
7 Machine used to surf the internet (8)
8 Half of four (3)
9 Buyer and seller (6)
10 At a low temperature (4)
11 Flowers (5)
13 Sleep (7)
15 Royal attendant (7)
17 The Hunter (constellation) (5)
21 Settee (4)
22 Ahead (6)
23 Kind or sort (3)
24 Card game (8)
25 Place of education (6)

Down

1 ___ shower: eg the Perseids (6)
2 Wears away (6)
3 Coldly (5)
4 Green gemstone (7)
5 Musical instrument with wire strings (8)
6 Turn into (6)
12 Grace (8)
14 Arsenal (7)
16 Allocations (6)
18 Deep blue colour (6)
19 Five cent coin (US) (6)
20 Hits swiftly (5)

No. 69

Across

1 Money in notes or coins (4)
3 Diabolical (8)
9 Loud and hoarse (7)
10 Lag behind (5)
11 Join together; merge (5)
12 Sully (7)
13 Package (6)
15 Swiss city (6)
17 ___ Bedingfield: musician (7)
18 Not suitable in the circumstances (5)
20 Angry (5)
21 Towards the future (7)
22 Mobster (8)
23 In a tense state (4)

Down

1 Communicating with (13)
2 ___ Arabia: country in the Middle East (5)
4 Not real or genuine (6)
5 Middleman (12)
6 Form a mental picture (7)
7 Unenthusiastically (4-9)
8 Vagrancy (12)
14 Learn new skills (7)
16 Confuse (6)
19 Eg an Oscar or Grammy (5)

No. 70

Across

1 Short-tempered (6)
4 Early spring flower (6)
9 Round building (7)
10 Largest anthropoid ape (7)
11 A score of two under par on a hole (golf) (5)
12 One who avoids animal products (5)
14 Supple (5)
15 Plants of a region (5)
17 More ashen in appearance (5)
18 Italian red wine (7)
20 Sour in taste (7)
21 Upper classes (6)
22 Courtroom officials (6)

Down

1 Arranged by type (6)
2 An engraved design (8)
3 Uptight (5)
5 Reprimand (7)
6 Cry out (4)
7 Wrench an ankle (6)
8 Dictatorial (11)
13 Easily deceived (8)
14 Wash and iron (7)
15 Fig can (anag) (6)
16 Constructs (6)
17 Removes the skin from (5)
19 Tehran is the capital here (4)

No. 71

Across

1 Woodwind instruments (5)
4 Among (7)
7 Electrician (5)
8 Re-evaluate (8)
9 Small pier (5)
11 Common salad dressing (5,3)
15 Find beer (anag) (8)
17 Detection technology (5)
19 Central American monkey (8)
20 Slopes (5)
21 Beginner (7)
22 Slap (5)

Down

1 Be too intense for (9)
2 Derived from living matter (7)
3 Breaks into pieces (7)
4 Art of growing dwarfed trees (6)
5 Relinquishment of a right (6)
6 Make a physical or mental effort (5)
10 Criterion (9)
12 Slight earthquakes (7)
13 Greek wine (7)
14 More moist (6)
16 Pencil rubber (6)
18 Not together (5)

No. 72

Across

1 Brown carbonated drink (4)
3 Move to another country (8)
9 Animal fat (7)
10 Find out (5)
11 Regather tins (anag) (12)
13 Consent to receive (6)
15 Explanation (6)
17 Blasphemous (12)
20 ___ Dushku: US actress (5)
21 Be too hot (7)
22 Most saccharine (8)
23 Individual article or unit (4)

Down

1 Gigantic (8)
2 Of the moon (5)
4 Eg March and May (6)
5 Birds of prey (6,6)
6 Flowering shrubs (7)
7 Volcano in Sicily (4)
8 Crucial (3,9)
12 Very small unit of length (8)
14 Cup (7)
16 Shuts (6)
18 Group of eight (5)
19 Precious stones; outstanding things (4)

No. 73

Across

1 State confidently (6)
5 Bed for a baby (3)
7 Slender woman or girl (5)
8 Modern type of paint (7)
9 Piece of information (5)
10 Locate exactly (8)
12 Reverses (6)
14 Body shape (6)
17 Disintegrate (8)
18 Suspends (5)
20 Trucks (7)
21 Animal life of a region (5)
22 ___ sauce: Chinese condiment (3)
23 Spatter in small drops (6)

Down

2 Subdivision (7)
3 Extension of a debt (8)
4 Lump of earth (4)
5 Country house (7)
6 Wood-eating insect (7)
7 Examines quickly (5)
11 Small landing and take-off area (8)
12 Mischievous children (7)
13 Make something seem worthy (7)
15 Critiques (7)
16 Musical instrument (5)
19 Slow-moving garden mollusc (4)

No. 74

1		2			3		4		5		6
				7							
8											
		9						10			
11			12			13					
				14							
15	16						17		18		19
						20					
21				22							
								23			
24											
					25						

Across

1 Shelves (6)
7 Aromatic spice (8)
8 Command to a horse (3)
9 Sloping (of a typeface) (6)
10 Statistics and facts (4)
11 Sweetener (5)
13 Insipidly (7)
15 Terrible (7)
17 Evade (5)
21 Effigy (4)
22 Dung beetle (6)
23 Chris ___ : English singer (3)
24 Brilliant musical performers (8)
25 Pursues (6)

Down

1 Devices that illuminate (6)
2 Changing the colour of hair (6)
3 Tell off (5)
4 ___ down: apply oneself to a task (7)
5 Spanish dance (8)
6 Youth ___ : accommodation provider (6)
12 Complete; utter (8)
14 Hearing range (7)
16 Blunt needle (6)
18 Scattered rubbish; brides (anag) (6)
19 Pieces of writing (6)
20 Conjuring trick (5)

No. 75

Across

1 Philosophical doctrine (11)
9 Small branch (5)
10 Large period of time (3)
11 Walk with an affected gait (5)
12 Stiff with age (5)
13 Scantily (8)
16 Formal agreement (8)
18 Underground enlarged stem (5)
21 Christina ___ : Addams Family actress (5)
22 Five plus five (3)
23 Principle laid down by an authority (5)
24 Administrations (11)

Down

2 Beg (7)
3 Great happiness (7)
4 Subject to death (6)
5 African country whose capital is Niamey (5)
6 Paces (5)
7 Revive (11)
8 Act of looking after children (11)
14 Patio area (7)
15 Beginning to exist (7)
17 Starting point (6)
19 Small tuned drum (5)
20 Natural elevation (5)

No. 76

Across

1 Corrected version (8)
5 Parched (4)
8 Directly opposite in character (5)
9 Part of a gun (7)
10 Install (7)
12 Melodious (7)
14 Tried a new product (7)
16 Variety show (7)
18 Tool that is useful for the Arctic (3,4)
19 Propel forwards (5)
20 Take a breath owing to astonishment (4)
21 Extravagant (8)

Down

1 Tears open (4)
2 Personal attendants (6)
3 Framework for moving the injured (9)
4 Popular soup flavour (6)
6 Style of popular music (6)
7 Made less bright (8)
11 Ran away en masse (of animals) (9)
12 Walking quickly (8)
13 Monks live in these (6)
14 Stroke (anag) (6)
15 Failing to win (6)
17 Meat from a calf (4)

79

No. 77

Across

1 Radiancy; gloss (5)
4 In the middle (7)
7 Heavy iron tool (5)
8 Decade from 1920 - 1929 (8)
9 Style of Greek architecture (5)
11 Rubbed with the hands (8)
15 Fellow Christians (8)
17 Religious doctrine (5)
19 Astronaut (8)
20 Cloud (anag) (5)
21 Thaw (7)
22 Drab (5)

Down

1 Feeling (9)
2 Cost (7)
3 Impartial (7)
4 Dairy product (6)
5 Type of muscle (6)
6 Excuse or pretext (5)
10 Sneakily (9)
12 Equipped (7)
13 Deep red colour (7)
14 Tentacle (6)
16 ___ Everett: English actor (6)
18 Run away with a lover (5)

No. 78

Across

1 Curved shape (4)
3 Trails alongside canals (8)
9 Had faith in (7)
10 Form of oxygen (5)
11 Someone who makes sweets (12)
13 Repudiate (6)
15 Emotional shock (6)
17 Omit too much detail (12)
20 Gave a job to (5)
21 A very skilled performer (7)
22 Lessening (8)
23 Network of lines (4)

Down

1 Come before in time (8)
2 Stir milk (5)
4 Eccentricity (6)
5 Cameraman (12)
6 Henry David ___ : US author and poet (7)
7 Garden outbuilding (4)
8 Dreamy; odd and unfamiliar (12)
12 Infancy (8)
14 More than two (7)
16 Pilot (6)
18 Inert (anag) (5)
19 Ostrichlike bird (4)

CROSSWORD

No. 79

Across

1 Exhausts (4)
3 Type of tooth (8)
9 Relating to Oxford (7)
10 Opposite of tall (5)
11 Science of biological processes (12)
14 Opposite of high (3)
16 Swerve; bend (5)
17 Mother (3)
18 Conjectural (12)
21 Embarrass (5)
22 Increased efficiency by working together (7)
23 Base of a statue (8)
24 Well-behaved (4)

Down

1 Increase rapidly (8)
2 Camera image (abbrev) (5)
4 ___ Botham: former cricketer (3)
5 Completely unaware of (12)
6 Schedule of activities (7)
7 Tiny specks (4)
8 Garments worn in bed (12)
12 Military walk (5)
13 In work (8)
15 Capricious; difficult to control (7)
19 Freight (5)
20 Type of light (4)
22 Expanse of salt water (3)

No. 80

Across

1 Rebuffed (8)
5 Land measure (4)
8 Strength (5)
9 Took the place of (7)
10 Inspire with love (7)
12 Hugs (7)
14 Plans (7)
16 Try (7)
18 Challenges the truth of (7)
19 Blunder (5)
20 International exhibition (4)
21 Remote; cut off (8)

Down

1 Cut of beef (4)
2 Stewed or boiled (6)
3 Violent upheaval (9)
4 Discharges (6)
6 Person who imprisons another (6)
7 Sanctions (8)
11 Divine messenger (9)
12 Imaginative (8)
13 Increase in intensity (4,2)
14 Stagnation or inactivity (6)
15 Outsider (6)
17 Sell (4)

No. 81

Across

1 Ship used by Jason and followers (4)
3 First public performance (8)
9 Variegated (7)
10 Mature person (5)
11 Particle that is electrically charged (3)
12 Extreme (5)
13 Intense light beam (5)
15 Defence of the ___ : David Drury movie (5)
17 ___ acid: protein building block (5)
18 Drowned river valley (3)
19 Mental impressions (5)
20 Remove or take out (7)
21 Channels of the nose (8)
22 TV award (4)

Down

1 Increase in signal power (13)
2 Obtain information from various sources (5)
4 Driers (anag) (6)
5 Calculations of dimensions (12)
6 Agreed or corresponded (7)
7 Wastefully; lavishly (13)
8 Troublemaker (6-6)
14 Flying vehicles without engines (7)
16 Be attractive (6)
18 Supply with new weapons (5)

No. 82

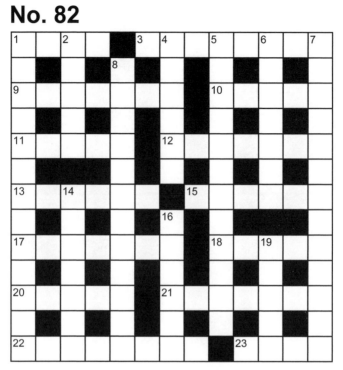

Across

1 Round before the final (abbrev) (4)
3 Complying with orders (8)
9 Pieces of correspondence sent through the post (7)
10 Woollen fabric (5)
11 ___ DeGeneres: US comedienne (5)
12 Geoffrey ___ : English poet (7)
13 ___ Goldberg: US actress (6)
15 Process food (6)
17 Dandier (anag) (7)
18 Old French currency (5)
20 Nationality of Louis Walsh (5)
21 Look something over (7)
22 Dress clothes (4,4)
23 Impose a tax (4)

Down

1 25th anniversary of marriage (6,7)
2 Roadside form of lodging (5)
4 Divide into two parts (6)
5 Displeased (12)
6 Aural pain (7)
7 Conceptually (13)
8 Miser (5-7)
14 Musical wind instrument (7)
16 Stefan ___ : Swedish tennis player (6)
19 Unconditional love (5)

No. 83

Across

1	Act of treachery (8)
5	Stylish and fashionable (4)
8	Folded back part of a coat (5)
9	Absence of sound (7)
10	Pack cue (anag) (7)
12	Get ready (7)
14	Satisfy; conciliate (7)
16	Commanded (7)
18	Copy; mimic (7)
19	Removes the lid (5)
20	Expel; drive out (4)
21	Rigidly; sternly (8)

Down

1	Male of a bovine mammal (4)
2	Walk very quietly (6)
3	Semiaquatic reptile (9)
4	Region of NE France (6)
6	Aircraft housing (6)
7	Acceptance of something as true (8)
11	Spicy sausage (9)
12	Horse of light tan colour (8)
13	Small whirlpools (6)
14	Season of the Church year (6)
15	Although (6)
17	Catch sight of (4)

No. 84

Across

1 Reasoned judgement (5)
4 Bridge above another road (7)
7 Bedfordshire town (5)
8 Large African mammals (8)
9 Ways or tracks (5)
11 Rocked (8)
15 Walks unsteadily (8)
17 Senior figure in a tribe (5)
19 Break in activity (8)
20 Deprive of weapons (5)
21 Warning device for ships (7)
22 Corrodes (5)

Down

1 Angular distance east or west (9)
2 Attic rooms (7)
3 Pleased (7)
4 Sheepskin (6)
5 Of the eye (6)
6 The beginning of an era (5)
10 Stupid (9)
12 Device that measures electric current (7)
13 Shore birds (7)
14 Scarcity (6)
16 Substance found in wine (6)
18 Foreign language (slang) (5)

No. 85

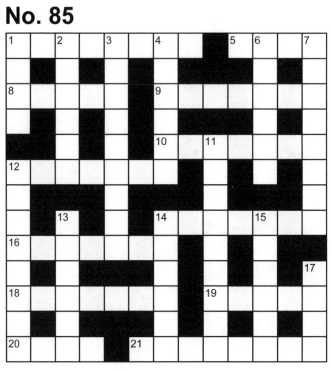

Across

1 Repugnance (8)
5 Where one finds Bamako (4)
8 Type of shelf (5)
9 Activity of travelling for pleasure (7)
10 Lived (7)
12 Disentangle (7)
14 Boastful person (7)
16 Concentrated on (7)
18 Enlist (7)
19 Female relation (5)
20 Ooze or leak slowly (4)
21 Fervently (8)

Down

1 Feels unwell (4)
2 First born (6)
3 How words are written on paper (9)
4 Vent (6)
6 Fly an aircraft (6)
7 Lacking humility (8)
11 Purity; lack of guile (9)
12 Specified work clothes (8)
13 Frozen water spear (6)
14 Newspaper boss (6)
15 Purpose (6)
17 Depend upon (4)

No. 86

Across

1	Production (11)
9	Perfect (5)
10	Ruction (3)
11	Spring flower (5)
12	Country in the Middle East (5)
13	North American diving ducks (8)
16	Neutral particle with negligible mass (8)
18	Pipes (5)
21	Pattern (5)
22	Not on (3)
23	Gives out (5)
24	Eternity (11)

Down

2	Burst violently (7)
3	Turned over (7)
4	Had a strong smell (6)
5	Narrow passageway (5)
6	Assert that something is the case (5)
7	Angry dispute (11)
8	Oppressed (11)
14	Hat with a wide brim (7)
15	Reroutes (7)
17	Eagles' nests (6)
19	Confuse or obscure (5)
20	Iron alloy (5)

No. 87

Across

1 Sagacious (6)
7 Salutation (8)
8 Long deep track (3)
9 A wine shop (6)
10 Simple non-flowering plant (4)
11 Woodland god (5)
13 Becomes less severe (7)
15 Obtain (7)
17 Legendary stories (5)
21 In case (4)
22 Reach (6)
23 Pair of people (3)
24 Traitor (8)
25 Straying from the right course (6)

Down

1 Commercial aircraft (6)
2 Tasty morsel (6)
3 Small heron (5)
4 Acted properly (7)
5 Plan of action (8)
6 Chess piece (6)
12 Boating (8)
14 Inventor (7)
16 Expressing regret (6)
18 Frozen plain (6)
19 Begin to grow (6)
20 Propose; utter (5)

No. 88

Across

1 Capturing (6)
4 Fashioned (6)
9 Entrust a secret to another (7)
10 Desist from (7)
11 Result (5)
12 Pains (5)
14 Pulpy (5)
15 First Greek letter (5)
17 Gnat (5)
18 Water container (7)
20 Female big cat (7)
21 Confer holy orders on (6)
22 Perceived (6)

Down

1 Heart (slang) (6)
2 Position of a male monarch (8)
3 Sound (5)
5 Midpoint (7)
6 Earnest appeal (4)
7 Dosing (anag) (6)
8 Allowed (11)
13 Careless (8)
14 Cocktail with gin and vermouth (7)
15 Having colourless skin (6)
16 Hired out (6)
17 Roger ___ : English actor (5)
19 Bound (4)

No. 89

Across

1 Piece of furniture (8)
5 Domestic felines (4)
9 Narrow valleys (5)
10 External (5)
11 Able to exist together without trouble (10)
14 Prayer (6)
15 Poser; enigma (6)
17 Not genuine (10)
20 Shadow (5)
21 State indirectly (5)
22 Sight organs (4)
23 Male relation (8)

Down

1 Listening devices (4)
2 Clive ___ : British Sin City actor (4)
3 Worldly (12)
4 Morsels of food (6)
6 Protein that neutralises an antigen (8)
7 Magician (8)
8 Donation (12)
12 Hairstyle (8)
13 Capable of being conquered (8)
16 Hot spice (6)
18 Primates (4)
19 Blue-green colour (4)

No. 90

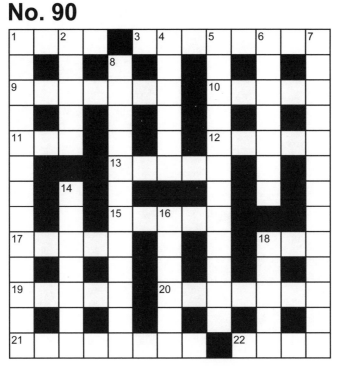

Across

1 Flexible containers (4)
3 Roomy (8)
9 Toxin in the body (7)
10 Royal (5)
11 Opposite of bottom (3)
12 Expect; think that (5)
13 Fabric (5)
15 Expressed clearly (5)
17 Surprise result (5)
18 Observe (3)
19 Nadir (anag) (5)
20 Furthest away (7)
21 Annoying with continual criticism (8)
22 Refuse to admit the truth of (4)

Down

1 Animal used for heavy work (5,2,6)
2 Rise (3,2)
4 Mexican cloak (6)
5 Major type of food nutrient (12)
6 Continuing (7)
7 Obviously (4-9)
8 Relating to farming (12)
14 Failure to be present (7)
16 Silky case of some insect larvae (6)
18 Twenty (5)

No. 91

Across

1 Thermosetting resin (5)
4 Afternoon theatre performance (7)
7 Large indefinite amount (5)
8 Wrapper for a letter (8)
9 Roman country house (5)
11 Emaciated (8)
15 Minute organisms in the sea (8)
17 Expulsion (5)
19 Tank for keeping fish (8)
20 Negatively charged ion (5)
21 One more (7)
22 Type of herring (5)

Down

1 Costly (9)
2 Laurence ___ : English actor (7)
3 Gave way to pressure (7)
4 Short-sightedness (6)
5 Make worse (6)
6 Praise enthusiastically (5)
10 Alteration (9)
12 Entrails (7)
13 Stirred (anag) (7)
14 Nearly (6)
16 Alcoholic drink (6)
18 Heavy noble gas (5)

No. 92

Across

1 Lesion (4)
3 Fragrant toiletries (8)
9 Act of turning up (7)
10 Clear and apparent (5)
11 Imitator (12)
13 Renounce (6)
15 ___ acid: lemon juice constituent (6)
17 Picture (12)
20 Performing a deed (5)
21 Tom Jones song (7)
22 City in NE Scotland (8)
23 Exercise venues (4)

Down

1 Huge ice masses (8)
2 Parts (anag) (5)
4 Wild West drinking room (6)
5 Vehemently (12)
6 Strident noise (7)
7 Trigonometric function (4)
8 Ate excessively (12)
12 Plant with decorative leaves (8)
14 Crash together (7)
16 Heavy food (6)
18 Printed insert supplied with a CD (5)
19 Thought (4)

CROSSWORD

No. 93

Across

1 Beast of burden (4)
3 Amaze (8)
9 Cotton fabric (7)
10 Allowed by official rules (5)
11 A sense (5)
12 Exceptional; not usual (7)
13 Periods of history (6)
15 Deletes (6)
17 Imprecise (7)
18 Piece of furniture (5)
20 Smallest quantity (5)
21 Person who keeps watch (7)
22 Submissive (8)
23 Russian monarch (4)

Down

1 Dictatorially (13)
2 Spear (5)
4 Added together (6)
5 Destruction (12)
6 Act of entering (7)
7 Fairground ride (6-7)
8 Showing complete commitment (12)
14 Intimidate (7)
16 Taken illegally (6)
19 Printed publications (5)

No. 94

Across

1 Kiln (4)
3 Formal evening dress (5,3)
9 As fast as possible (4,3)
10 Horse's cry (5)
11 Person recovering from an illness (12)
13 Style of art or architecture (6)
15 Type of cloud (6)
17 Unkind; unsympathetic (12)
20 Reel for winding yarn (5)
21 Small storage rooms or cupboards (7)
22 Cloudy (8)
23 Heavenly body (4)

Down

1 People holding positions of authority (8)
2 European country (5)
4 Alphabetical character (6)
5 Compulsory military service (12)
6 Narrower (7)
7 Sound reflection (4)
8 Not intoxicating (of a drink) (12)
12 Appraiser; valuer (8)
14 Sanction something reluctantly (7)
16 Lorries (6)
18 Sheep sound (5)
19 Capital of Norway (4)

No. 95

Across

1 Plant with oil rich seeds (6)
4 Toughen (6)
9 Not as old (7)
10 Driving out (7)
11 Nursemaid (5)
12 Valuable thing or person (5)
14 Incantation (5)
15 Should (5)
17 Metal worker (5)
18 Let in to a place again (7)
20 Separated; remote (7)
21 Doglike mammals (6)
22 What a spider makes (6)

Down

1 Throwing at a target (6)
2 Of striking beauty (8)
3 Humid (5)
5 At the ocean floor (7)
6 ___ Moore: US actress (4)
7 Type of confectionery (6)
8 Posing a difficulty (11)
13 Husband of one's daughter (3-2-3)
14 Endurance (7)
15 Surge forwards (6)
16 Winged child (6)
17 Stage name of Mark Althavean Andrews (5)
19 Peas (anag) (4)

No. 96

Across

1 Qualifications (8)
5 Con; swindle (4)
9 Gold measure (5)
10 Baking appliances (5)
11 Person who makes iron goods (10)
14 Paired (anag) (6)
15 Large insect (6)
17 Meticulous (10)
20 Electronic communication (5)
21 Care for; look after (5)
22 Appear to be (4)
23 Ability to float (8)

Down

1 Eat like a bird (4)
2 Belonging to us (4)
3 Comprehensible (12)
4 Express disagreement (6)
6 Relating to office work (8)
7 Title of a newspaper (8)
8 Body of voters in a specified region (12)
12 Puts forward for acceptance (8)
13 Religious deserter (8)
16 One's environment (6)
18 Tiny bird (4)
19 Wet with condensation (4)

No. 97

Across

1 Action of ending a partnership (11)
9 Rice dish (5)
10 ___ de Cologne: perfume (3)
11 Japanese dish (5)
12 Eg spaghetti (5)
13 Popular fizzy beverage (8)
16 Starved (8)
18 Puts through a sieve (5)
21 Musical speeds (5)
22 Strange (3)
23 Escape from (5)
24 Stargazers (11)

Down

2 Annoying (7)
3 Having great wisdom (7)
4 Drooped (6)
5 Solid blow (5)
6 Sets of six balls (cricket) (5)
7 Disenchant (11)
8 Fully settled (3,3,5)
14 Trimmed (anag) (7)
15 Glisten (7)
17 Season after summer (6)
19 Loses colour (5)
20 Give a solemn oath (5)

No. 98

Across

1 Extinct bird (4)
3 Fed to completeness (8)
9 Misconception (7)
10 Chris ___ : DJ and TV presenter (5)
11 Imposing poems (5)
12 ___ to: disagreeing with (7)
13 Urge (6)
15 Black Sea peninsula (6)
17 Vehement denunciations (7)
18 Upright (5)
20 ___ Camera: Scottish band (5)
21 Engraving (7)
22 Encrypting (8)
23 Second-hand (4)

Down

1 Distinguish between (13)
2 New ___ : Indian capital (5)
4 In a careless manner (6)
5 Lack of practical knowledge (12)
6 Crossbar set above a window (7)
7 Deprived (13)
8 Made in bulk (4-8)
14 Nonconformist (7)
16 Towards the rear (6)
19 Lives (anag) (5)

CROSSWORD

No. 99

Across

1 Piece of code to automate a task (5)
4 Oppressive rulers (7)
7 Low carts (5)
8 Toneless (anag) (8)
9 Mediterranean island (5)
11 Bushy-tailed rodent (8)
15 Re-emerge (8)
17 Saying (5)
19 Secret relationships (8)
20 Device used to sharpen razors (5)
21 A Roman Catholic devotion (7)
22 Not a winner (5)

Down

1 Metallic element (9)
2 Map line showing equal height (7)
3 Stablemen (7)
4 Scrap (6)
5 Antenna (6)
6 Secret rendezvous (5)
10 Person that attacks another first (9)
12 Relating to sight (7)
13 Pulls back from (7)
14 Serving no functional purpose (6)
16 Has objective reality (6)
18 Denise van ___ : English actress (5)

No. 100

Across

1 Pointers (anag) (8)
5 Large deer (pl) (4)
8 Too bright in colour (5)
9 Certificate (7)
10 Division of the UK (7)
12 In addition to (7)
14 Suggested a course of action (7)
16 Moaned (7)
18 Male chicken (7)
19 Hard chalcedony (5)
20 24 hour periods (4)
21 Harshness of manner (8)

Down

1 Long and thin piece of wood (4)
2 Female monster (6)
3 Soft quilt (9)
4 Pokes gently (6)
6 Bath sponge (6)
7 Reference point; norm (8)
11 Be attracted to a person or thing (9)
12 Pestered constantly (8)
13 No one (6)
14 Makes more attractive (6)
15 Highly seasoned sausage (6)
17 Large group of people (4)

CROSSWORD

No. 101

Across

1	Bend or coil (4)
3	Applauding (8)
9	Alternative forms of genes (7)
10	Irritate (5)
11	Teach to accept a belief uncritically (12)
13	Sadness (6)
15	Pantry (6)
17	Carefree (5-2-5)
20	Dramatic musical work (5)
21	Dishonourable (7)
22	Floating masses of frozen water (8)
23	European mountain range (4)

Down

1	Personal magnetism (8)
2	Governed (5)
4	Surface coating (6)
5	Smooth and easy progress (5,7)
6	Caused to burn (7)
7	Men (4)
8	Coat with a metal (12)
12	Dullness of colour (8)
14	Triangle with three unequal sides (7)
16	Getting older (6)
18	Inner circle (5)
19	Large desert in Asia (4)

No. 102

Across

1 Neck-warming garments (6)
4 Not written in any key (of music) (6)
9 Constantly present (7)
10 Wax sticks used for drawing (7)
11 Golf shots (5)
12 Daisy-like flower (5)
14 White soft limestone (5)
15 Hit with the fist (5)
17 Small bottles (5)
18 Hot wind blowing from North Africa (7)
20 Planet (7)
21 Putting down carefully (6)
22 Promotional material (6)

Down

1 Area of flat unforested grassland (6)
2 Arithmetic operation (8)
3 Exhaust gases (5)
5 Fusion chamber (7)
6 Roman emperor (4)
7 Inferior (6)
8 Jobs (11)
13 Value greatly (8)
14 Register at a hotel (5,2)
15 Relating to the mail system (6)
16 Feature (6)
17 Lacking interest (5)
19 Optimistic (4)

No. 103

Across

1 ___ Novello: Welsh composer and actor (4)
3 Vehicle with one wheel (8)
9 Foot support for a rider (7)
10 Speech sound (5)
11 In a persuasive manner (12)
14 Knock vigorously (3)
16 Throw forcefully (5)
17 In favour of (3)
18 List of books referred to (12)
21 Firearm (5)
22 Perennial herb (7)
23 Fence of stakes (8)
24 Immerse in liquid (4)

Down

1 Lacking confidence (8)
2 Edible pungent bulb (5)
4 Bite sharply (3)
5 Popular district in London (6,6)
6 European primula (7)
7 ___ Macpherson: Australian supermodel (4)
8 Productivity (12)
12 Capital of Egypt (5)
13 Exterior of a motor vehicle (8)
15 Hurtful (7)
19 Musical instrument (5)
20 Prod (anag) (4)
22 Ancient (3)

No. 104

Across

1 Conclude; deduce (5)
4 Mound made by insects (7)
7 Crime of burning something (5)
8 Oily (8)
9 Anaemic-looking (5)
11 Explosive shells (8)
15 Large retail store (8)
17 Act of stealing (5)
19 Court of justice (8)
20 English county where one finds Chelmsford (5)
21 Ugly building (7)
22 Frightening (5)

Down

1 Rebel (9)
2 Grouped together (7)
3 Rebuttal (7)
4 Entice or attract (6)
5 Pester (6)
6 Not tight (5)
10 Royal mint (anag) (9)
12 Precludes (7)
13 Mechanical keyboard (7)
14 Makes available for sale (6)
16 Nautical (6)
18 Hurried (5)

No. 105

Across

1 Eg Queen of Hearts (7,4)
9 Entice to do something (5)
10 Exclamation of surprise (3)
11 Tree of the birch family with toothed leaves (5)
12 Adhesive (5)
13 Defeat thoroughly (8)
16 All-round view (8)
18 Gains possession of (5)
21 Male parent (5)
22 Pen point (3)
23 Stadium (5)
24 Style of painting (8,3)

Down

2 Directing (7)
3 Chemical element (7)
4 Type of rain cloud (6)
5 Destroy (3,2)
6 Large quantities of paper (5)
7 Unintentional (11)
8 Small garden cart (11)
14 Closely packed together (7)
15 Spouse (7)
17 Single-celled organism (6)
19 Skewered meat (5)
20 Begin (5)

No. 106

Across

1 Money that is owed (4)
3 Term for a pet feline (8)
9 Plunder (7)
10 Suffuse with colour (5)
11 Beginning (12)
13 Sampled (food) (6)
15 Gets together (6)
17 Advance payment (12)
20 Large wading bird (5)
21 Dilemma (7)
22 Prayer service (8)
23 Spheres (4)

Down

1 Give entirely to a cause (8)
2 Broom made of twigs (5)
4 Set free or release (6)
5 Lido (8,4)
6 Piece of furniture (7)
7 Adolescent (abbrev) (4)
8 Despair (12)
12 Giant ocean waves (8)
14 Not a ___ : nothing at all (7)
16 Visit informally (4,2)
18 Lazy person; layabout (5)
19 Throb (4)

No. 107

Across

1 Absorbent cloths (6)
7 Maritime (8)
8 Belonging to him (3)
9 Involuntary spasm (6)
10 Deliberately taunt (4)
11 This date (5)
13 Taken as true (7)
15 Arrogant person (7)
17 Evil spirit (5)
21 Particles around a comet (4)
22 Desires what another has (6)
23 Rocky hill (3)
24 Disloyal person (8)
25 Units of heat (6)

Down

1 Lightweight garment (1-5)
2 Desired (6)
3 Light meal (5)
4 Goal; intention (7)
5 Device for spraying paint (8)
6 Easily done (6)
12 Mammal with a sticky tongue (8)
14 Brutality (7)
16 For the time being (3,3)
18 Bivalve mollusc (6)
19 Scottish landowners (6)
20 Prevent (5)

No. 108

CROSSWORD

Across

1	Sleeveless cloak; headland (4)
3	Talking (8)
9	Uncommon (7)
10	Swift (5)
11	Next (12)
14	Former measure of length (3)
16	Mother-of-pearl (5)
17	Ate (anag) (3)
18	Unofficially (3,3,6)
21	___ Tuck: friend of Robin Hood (5)
22	Last longer than (7)
23	Frequent customers (8)
24	English public school (4)

Down

1	More awkward (8)
2	Ball of lead (5)
4	Friend (3)
5	Agreements; plans (12)
6	Sudden inclination to act (7)
7	Deities (4)
8	Occult (12)
12	Male relation (5)
13	Chinese language (8)
15	Raising (7)
19	Not concealed (5)
20	At a distance (4)
22	Belonging to us (3)

No. 109

Across

1 Escrow (anag) (6)
7 Lenience (8)
8 First woman (3)
9 One who has a salary (6)
10 Matures (4)
11 Peak (5)
13 Observed (7)
15 Cleaning item (7)
17 Senseless (5)
21 So be it (4)
22 Mystery; riddle (6)
23 Eg English Breakfast (3)
24 Vacillating (8)
25 Ukrainian port (6)

Down

1 Religious leader (6)
2 Respire with difficulty (6)
3 Barely sufficient (5)
4 A long time ago (4,3)
5 Denial of something (8)
6 Plan of action (6)
12 Spend wastefully (8)
14 Greek goddess of retribution (7)
16 Fighting between armed forces (6)
18 Lessens (6)
19 Printed mistakes (6)
20 Game of chance (5)

No. 110

Across

1 You usually do this whilst asleep (5)
4 Adult (5-2)
7 Garners (5)
8 French bread stick (8)
9 Neck warmer (5)
11 One who inspires others (8)
15 Closing the eyes momentarily (8)
17 Parody (5)
19 Affecting the emotions (8)
20 Academy Award (5)
21 Imaginary (7)
22 Gardeners sow these (5)

Down

1 Certainly (9)
2 Final stage of a process (7)
3 ___ Klass: TV presenter (7)
4 Stringed instrument (6)
5 Twist suddenly (6)
6 Opposite of lower (5)
10 Scares (9)
12 People of noble birth (7)
13 Tall quadruped (7)
14 Metallic element (6)
16 Appeared indistinctly (6)
18 Show-off (5)

No. 111

Across

1 Hunting dogs (6)
4 Ready ___ : flavour of crisps (6)
9 Wavering vocal quality (7)
10 Force of civilians trained as soldiers (7)
11 Competes in a speed contest (5)
12 Inactive (5)
14 Fabric used to make jeans (5)
15 ___ Adkins: English singer (5)
17 Search rigorously for (5)
18 Capital of Kenya (7)
20 Late (7)
21 Rarely encountered (6)
22 Men's tight fitting hat (6)

Down

1 Remains in one place in the air (6)
2 Unstrap (8)
3 Leads (anag) (5)
5 Praise strongly (7)
6 Tense (4)
7 Pour from one container to another (6)
8 Mixture (11)
13 Give someone the courage to do something (8)
14 Popular or colloquial (7)
15 Historical records (6)
16 Current of air (6)
17 View; picture (5)
19 ___ Fisher: actress (4)

No. 112

Across

1 Relax and do little (4)
3 Stringed musical instrument (8)
9 Become wrinkled (7)
10 Brazilian dance (5)
11 In accordance with general custom (12)
13 Encrypt (6)
15 Passion (6)
17 Mentally acute (5-7)
20 Fabric with parallel ribs (5)
21 Line that touches a curve (7)
22 Curative medicines; sets right (8)
23 ___ Sharif: Egyptian actor (4)

Down

1 Rebound (8)
2 Reject with disdain (5)
4 Representatives (6)
5 Disheartening (12)
6 Back pain (7)
7 Tidy (4)
8 Stretched out completely (12)
12 Person owed money (8)
14 Element needed by the body (7)
16 Tropical fly (6)
18 Unit of heat (5)
19 Agitate (4)

No. 113

Across

1 One who held a job previously (11)
9 Extremely small (prefix) (5)
10 Small numbered cube (3)
11 Furnish or supply (5)
12 Shyly (5)
13 Piece of paper money (4,4)
16 Self-operating machines (8)
18 Competed in a speed contest (5)
21 Country once ruled by Papa Doc (5)
22 Boolean operator (3)
23 Stringed instrument (5)
24 Shameful (11)

Down

2 Comes back (7)
3 Curbing (7)
4 Official seal or mark (6)
5 Indifferent to emotions (5)
6 Strangely (5)
7 Domineering (11)
8 Depletion of bodily fluids (11)
14 Small place of refuge (7)
15 Reindeer (7)
17 Country in Africa with capital Kampala (6)
19 Welsh breed of dog (5)
20 Remove errors from software (5)

No. 114

Across

1 Not hard (4)
3 Hamper (8)
9 Mundane (7)
10 Moves its wings (of a bird) (5)
11 Thoroughly (12)
13 Item of neckwear (6)
15 Hospital carers (6)
17 Sound of quick light steps (6-6)
20 Suspend; prevent (5)
21 Metal projectiles (7)
22 Hypothesise (8)
23 Circle around the head of a saint (4)

Down

1 Wisdom (8)
2 Foam (5)
4 Subtle detail (6)
5 Adverse (12)
6 Small hounds (7)
7 Justin ___ : golfer (4)
8 Maker (12)
12 Strong coffee (8)
14 Friendly (7)
16 Diving birds (6)
18 Eighth Greek letter (5)
19 Change (4)

CROSSWORD

No. 115

Across

1. Phrases that are not taken literally (6)
5. Before the present (of time) (3)
7. Beneath (5)
8. Young children (7)
9. Loutish person (5)
10. Light brown cane sugar (8)
12. Valuable things; strengths (6)
14. Toffees or chocolates (6)
17. Deluge (8)
18. Gets less difficult (5)
20. Friendless (7)
21. Discourage (5)
22. Strong alkaline solution (3)
23. Game bird; grumble (6)

Down

2. Paul ___ : British magician (7)
3. Opposite of majority (8)
4. Small whirlpool (4)
5. One of two gaps in a shirt (7)
6. Tentacled cephalopod (7)
7. Take illegally (5)
11. Fraudster (8)
12. Armoury (7)
13. Let up (7)
15. Rags (7)
16. Bring on oneself (5)
19. Locate or place (4)

No. 116

Across

1 Minute surface opening (4)
3 Small pellet put in among stored garments (8)
9 Part of a chair (7)
10 Book leaves (5)
11 Style of piano-based blues (6-6)
13 Offhand (6)
15 ___ City: where Batman lives (6)
17 Act of removing restrictions (12)
20 Parts of the cerebrum (5)
21 Warning (7)
22 Explode (8)
23 Arthur ___ : former US tennis player (4)

Down

1 Reproduce recorded sound (4,4)
2 Lover of Juliet (5)
4 Capital of Canada (6)
5 Thick-skinned herbivorous animal (12)
6 Great suffering (7)
7 Not as much (4)
8 Type of food shop (12)
12 Distinction (8)
14 Sweet effervescent powder (7)
16 Melodious (6)
18 Climbing shrubs (5)
19 Delighted (4)

CROSSWORD

No. 117

Across

1 Huge groups of insects (6)
5 Feather scarf (3)
7 Fish-eating mammal (5)
8 Decorated (7)
9 Existing (5)
10 Full measure of a drink (8)
12 Liveliness (6)
14 Concurred (6)
17 Changed (8)
18 Employing (5)
20 Insurance calculator (7)
21 Attach to (5)
22 Our star (3)
23 Pointed projectiles (6)

Down

2 Walks like a duck (7)
3 Main cost (anag) (8)
4 Remnant (4)
5 Written language for blind people (7)
6 Arranged neatly (7)
7 Smell (5)
11 Sparkling (8)
12 Makes certain of (7)
13 Large web-footed bird (7)
15 Raise an ___ : show surprise (7)
16 Compound used in making glass (5)
19 Unit of heredity (4)

No. 118

Across

1 Sea rescue vessel (8)
5 Look slyly (4)
8 Underground railway (5)
9 Large fortified buildings (7)
10 A deified mortal (7)
12 Settle a dispute (7)
14 Disentangle (7)
16 Distant runner-up in a horse race (4-3)
18 Lines of equal pressure on maps (7)
19 U-shaped curve in a river (5)
20 Gardening tools used for weeding (4)
21 Thing serving as an appropriate model (8)

Down

1 Green citrus fruit (4)
2 Made to fill a space precisely (6)
3 Person who takes bets (9)
4 Area with coin-operated games (6)
6 Expression of praise (6)
7 Remaining (8)
11 Universe as a whole (9)
12 Stone of great size (8)
13 On land (6)
14 For men and women (of clothing) (6)
15 Oral (6)
17 Large jug (4)

No. 119

Across

1 Paul ___ : former England football captain (4)
3 Sears (8)
9 Bring to life (7)
10 Aperture in the eye (5)
11 Drivel; nonsense (3)
12 Hank of wool (5)
13 Peers (5)
15 Ellipses (5)
17 Push away (5)
18 Excellent serve (3)
19 With a forward motion (5)
20 Pear-shaped fruit (7)
21 Admired and respected (8)
22 Limbs used for walking (4)

Down

1 Not proper (13)
2 Compress into small folds (5)
4 Intelligent (6)
5 Reclamation (12)
6 Unfortunate (7)
7 Magnificent (13)
8 A perfumed liquid (3,2,7)
14 Highest (7)
16 Wear away (6)
18 Confound (5)

No. 120

Across

- **1** Reducing to small particles (8)
- **5** Freshwater game fish (4)
- **9** Dull colours (5)
- **10** Sheltered places (5)
- **11** Complete devotion (10)
- **14** Speaks (6)
- **15** Carols (anag) (6)
- **17** Temperature scale (10)
- **20** Small boat (5)
- **21** Pollex (5)
- **22** Office table (4)
- **23** Branch of mathematics (8)

Down

- **1** Jokes (4)
- **2** Wild mountain goat (4)
- **3** Dispirited (12)
- **4** Table linen (6)
- **6** Young ruffian (8)
- **7** Commerce (8)
- **8** Unfriendly (12)
- **12** Came to light (8)
- **13** Engravings (8)
- **16** Playing period in polo (6)
- **18** Contest between two people (4)
- **19** Large wading bird (4)

No. 121

Across

1 Farming tool (6)
7 Leonardo ___ : actor (8)
8 Mischievous sprite (3)
9 Extreme scarcity of food (6)
10 Challenge (4)
11 Distorts (5)
13 Remnant (7)
15 Not connected to the internet (7)
17 Body of water (5)
21 Eg an arm or leg (4)
22 Opposite of an acid (6)
23 ___ Tyler: actress (3)
24 Yellowish edible seed (8)
25 Detects; feels (6)

Down

1 Change rapidly from one position to another (6)
2 Strongbox for valuables (6)
3 ___ Izzard: English comedian (5)
4 Long speeches (7)
5 Large outbreak of a disease (8)
6 Millionth of a metre (6)
12 Withdraw (4,4)
14 Sad (7)
16 Journey by air (6)
18 Those expelled from a country (6)
19 These relay bodily messages (6)
20 Seabirds (5)

No. 122

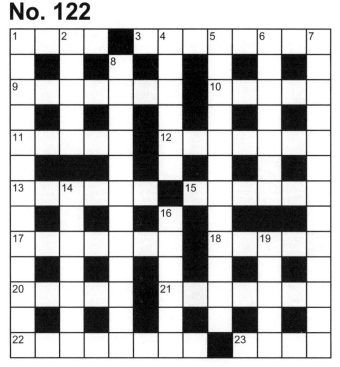

Across

1 Too; in addition (4)
3 Green vegetable (8)
9 Wavering effect in a musical tone (7)
10 Insurgent or revolutionary (5)
11 Start of something (5)
12 Agrees or corresponds (7)
13 Innate (6)
15 Stableman (6)
17 Evaded (7)
18 Refute by evidence (5)
20 Country in southern Asia (5)
21 Ban on publication (7)
22 Gibberish (8)
23 Snake-like fish (4)

Down

1 Official permission (13)
2 Plant stalks (5)
4 Firmly established (6)
5 Restrict within limits (12)
6 Passing around a town (of a road) (7)
7 Pictures (13)
8 Person studying after a first degree (12)
14 Widen (7)
16 Venomous snakes (6)
19 Long flat-bottomed boat (5)

No. 123

Across

1 Froth of soap and water (4)
3 Religion (8)
9 Area of London (4,3)
10 Flower part (5)
11 Commensurate (12)
13 Step down from a job (6)
15 Small cave (6)
17 Constantly; always (12)
20 Australian arboreal marsupial (5)
21 Fish tanks (7)
22 Playhouses (8)
23 Fervour (4)

Down

1 Supporting railway track beams (8)
2 Dance club (5)
4 Modernise (6)
5 Ill-mannered (12)
6 Insert in a person's body (7)
7 Dairy product (4)
8 Medicine taken when blocked-up (12)
12 Hairstyle (8)
14 Electronic retention of data (7)
16 Get away from (6)
18 Number in a trio (5)
19 Comedy sketch (4)

No. 124

Across

1 Unwell (4)
3 Worldwide outbreak (8)
9 Fatuously (7)
10 Vends (5)
11 Happiness (12)
14 Plant fluid (3)
16 Strike firmly (5)
17 23rd Greek letter (3)
18 Unseasonably warm period (6,6)
21 Cake decoration (5)
22 Accommodation (7)
23 Plantation producing grapes (8)
24 Surprise; amaze (4)

Down

1 Luggage item (8)
2 ___ Balding: TV presenter (5)
4 ___ Winehouse: singer (3)
5 Insincere (12)
6 Coward (7)
7 Snug (4)
8 Invigoratingly (12)
12 Labour organisation (5)
13 Atmospheric gas (8)
15 Regular payment made to a retired person (7)
19 Damp (5)
20 Capital of the Ukraine (4)
22 Female pronoun (3)

CROSSWORD

No. 125

Across

1 Medical practitioner (6)
4 Elongated rectangle (6)
9 Group of figures representing a scene (7)
10 Sturdy thickset canine (7)
11 Empty spaces (5)
12 The spirit of a people (5)
14 Happen (5)
15 Greek writer of fables (5)
17 Father (5)
18 Upstart; one who has recently gained wealth (7)
20 Seedless raisin (7)
21 Catch or snare (6)
22 Get by with (4,2)

Down

1 Grammatical case (6)
2 Small bays (8)
3 Last Greek letter (5)
5 Constructor (7)
6 Roman poet (4)
7 Sacred river of India (6)
8 Inn (6,5)
13 Individually crafted by a person (8)
14 Character in Hamlet (7)
15 Of high mountains (6)
16 Electric generator (6)
17 Triangular river mouth (5)
19 Corrode (4)

No. 126

Across

1 Chair at the rear of a vehicle (4,4)
5 Venerable ___ : English monk (4)
9 Absolute (5)
10 Subside (5)
11 Share out (10)
14 Award (6)
15 Group of six (6)
17 Causing irritation (10)
20 Egg-shaped (5)
21 Manipulate dough (5)
22 Longest river (4)
23 Reads out (8)

Down

1 Greatest (4)
2 US pop star (4)
3 Uncurled (12)
4 Wards off (6)
6 Appraise (8)
7 ___ hour: the latest possible moment (8)
8 Skilled joiner (12)
12 Resolute (8)
13 Soccer (8)
16 Respiratory condition (6)
18 Encounter a person (4)
19 Appends (4)

No. 127

Across

1 Takes an exam (4)
3 Dishes that begin a meal (8)
9 One event in a sequence (7)
10 Temporary stop (5)
11 Person who flies an aircraft (5)
12 Latter part of the day (7)
13 Foolish person (6)
15 Untape (anag) (6)
17 Back up (7)
18 Robber (5)
20 Rock group (5)
21 Remedy for everything (7)
22 Writer of literary works (8)
23 Stained a fabric or hair (4)

Down

1 Any means of advancement (8,5)
2 Quavering sound (5)
4 Set in layers (6)
5 Symbolising (12)
6 Act of avoiding capture (7)
7 Legerdemain (7,2,4)
8 Luckily (12)
14 Computer keyboard users (7)
16 Ear bone (6)
19 Needing to be scratched (5)

No. 128

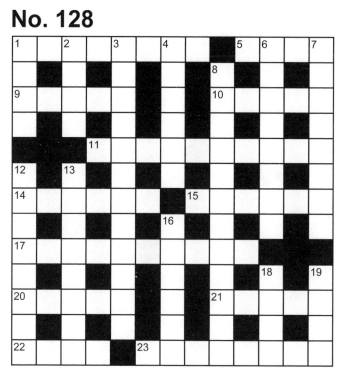

Across

1 Opposites (8)
5 Ship's complement (4)
9 Twilled cotton fabric (5)
10 Approaches (5)
11 Reduce speed (10)
14 Cause to fall from a horse (6)
15 Scattered about (6)
17 Female attendant at a wedding (10)
20 Armature of an electric motor (5)
21 People who are greatly admired (5)
22 Jedi Master in Star Wars films (4)
23 Dawdlers (8)

Down

1 Imperial unit (4)
2 Head covering (4)
3 Large Brazilian city (3,2,7)
4 US rapper (6)
6 Rouse again (8)
7 Cowboy films (8)
8 Amusing (12)
12 Type of edible fruit (8)
13 Aided (8)
16 Leaping antelope (6)
18 Sullen (4)
19 Requests (4)

CROSSWORD

No. 129

Across

1 Falls back (4)
3 Pertaining to Spain (8)
9 Vital content (7)
10 Small antelope (5)
11 Passenger ship (5)
12 Aperture or hole (7)
13 Unit of time (6)
15 Nerve cell (6)
17 Meaninglessness (7)
18 Make fun of someone (5)
20 Variety or kind (5)
21 Attains (7)
22 Christmas season (8)
23 Biblical garden (4)

Down

1 Eternally (13)
2 Sea crew member (5)
4 Refrigerator compartment (6)
5 Fortunate; opportune (12)
6 Less quiet (7)
7 British comic writer and comedian (5,8)
8 Inflexible (12)
14 Water passage (7)
16 Composite of different species (6)
19 Plant pest (5)

No. 130

Across

1 Sudden desire (4)
3 Imitator (8)
9 Shock with wonder (7)
10 Humped ruminant (5)
11 Easy-going (4-8)
13 Forces out (6)
15 Revolve quickly (6)
17 Baked product containing seasoned meat (7,5)
20 Word of farewell (5)
21 Existing at the beginning (7)
22 Announce publicly (8)
23 Small vipers (4)

Down

1 Quarrels (8)
2 Prologue (abbrev) (5)
4 Title used for a French woman (6)
5 As quickly as possible (7-5)
6 Painting medium (7)
7 Small stream (4)
8 Knowing more than one language (12)
12 Uses again (8)
14 Stipulation (7)
16 Birthplace of St Francis (6)
18 Nationality of Stanislas Wawrinka (5)
19 Part of a door fastening (4)

No. 131

Across

1 Story (4)
3 Scrawl (8)
9 Issue forth (7)
10 Eat quickly (5)
11 Where one finds Rome (5)
12 Scarf (7)
13 Irrelevant pieces of information (6)
15 Middle (6)
17 Light two-wheeled motor vehicle (7)
18 Savoury jelly (5)
20 Makhaya ___ : South African cricketer (5)
21 Criminal (7)
22 Opposite of westerly (8)
23 ___ Campbell: Scream actress (4)

Down

1 Horror film directed by M Night Shyamalan (3,5,5)
2 South American animal (5)
4 Very milky (6)
5 Intolerable (12)
6 Pamphlet (7)
7 Fizz (13)
8 Intricate and confusing (12)
14 Traditional piano keys (7)
16 Small stones (6)
19 Shallow circular dish (5)

No. 132

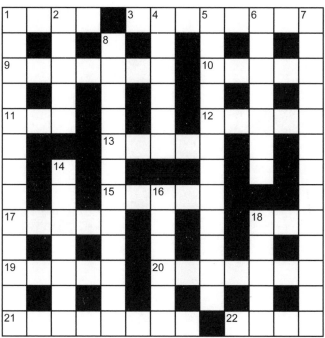

Across

1 Temporary living quarters (4)
3 Wine and soda water mix (8)
9 Becomes less wide (7)
10 Move slowly (5)
11 Frozen water (3)
12 Loop with a running knot (5)
13 Tests (5)
15 Grows weary (5)
17 Pertaining to the ear (5)
18 Pasture; meadow (3)
19 Interior (5)
20 Lock of curly hair (7)
21 Someone with the same moniker (8)
22 Mark left from a wound (4)

Down

1 Shape or arrangement (13)
2 ___ Simpson: cartoon character (5)
4 Former Spanish currency (6)
5 Not staying the same throughout (12)
6 Very enthusiastic (7)
7 Amusement park ride (6,7)
8 Upper chamber in Parliament (5,2,5)
14 Kind of abbreviation (7)
16 Jacket (6)
18 Sweet-scented shrub (5)

No. 133

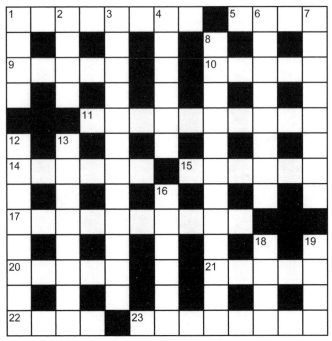

Across

1 Official orders (8)
5 Business (4)
9 Item of cutlery (5)
10 Original; new (5)
11 Corporations (10)
14 King's son (6)
15 Body of work (6)
17 Unable to count (10)
20 Apprehended with certainty (5)
21 Under (5)
22 Compass point (4)
23 Most precipitous (8)

Down

1 Facial disguise (4)
2 Noble gas (4)
3 Formal notice (12)
4 Excitingly strange (6)
6 Intrusive (8)
7 Thick dark syrup (8)
8 Not discernible (12)
12 Scatter in drops (8)
13 Woody (8)
16 Intense feeling of fear (6)
18 Merriment (4)
19 Study assiduously (4)

No. 134

Across

1 Slightly annoyed (6)
4 Peevish (6)
9 A score less four (7)
10 One who holds property for another (7)
11 Creamy-white colour (5)
12 Teams (5)
14 Spiny yellow plant (5)
15 Henrik ___ : Norwegian dramatist (5)
17 Reclining (5)
18 Salt lake in the Jordan valley (4,3)
20 Cut of beef (7)
21 Lower (6)
22 Assumed propositions (6)

Down

1 Believer in the occult (6)
2 Places of refuge (8)
3 Military opponent (5)
5 Drive back by force (7)
6 Rubber overshoe (4)
7 Songlike cries (6)
8 Put questions to (11)
13 Disordered state of mind (8)
14 Costing (anag) (7)
15 Situated within a building (6)
16 A way out (6)
17 Slight error; oversight (5)
19 Chopped; cancelled (4)

137

SOLUTIONS

Solution 1

```
P E S T   S C R A M B L E
R T A   A C   R   M
I C I C L E S   C L I M B
M N P   I   I T   E
E G G   H N D R A W L
M     A D O R E   I L
I   E B   N   N   I
N X E X A C T   S
I N P U T   D A   A S H
S A   I   A L P   M
T O N I C   P I L L A G E
E D   A T   Y C   N
R E S T L E S S   L E F T
```

Solution 2

```
C O U N T S   R U B R I C
O N A C M   O   L
M O R O C C O P   A O
P A K M A T U R E S
E L V I S P E   E
L E   O E A S E D
L O L S E N A
N O S E S I   T S
O M T M A I Z E
R A V I O L I E A C
D I S O C T O B E R
I S I N E L E
C O A R S E A R G E N T
```

Solution 3

```
I N S T I G A T O R S
I E W I O E D
I N A O R B I T S U E
T O R U S B A E N
E E O E L O T T O
R O S E M A R Y M
P T E B V I
R A U T O B A H N
E R A S E M L N A
T D X L S M E L T O
E W E C H A R T S O
D P E U E S R
U T I L I T A R I A N
```

Solution 4

```
C U R V E S A V E
H I C I S T E R N S
O R C R P N J
O H A W A I I D H O W
S E P R E I
E A S E L L I S T I N G
M L N T
C O W B O Y S P A W E D
L I R S I O
L I F T I N T E N D C
V T C E E L K
L E V E R A G E S E
S R L P E W T E R
```

Solution 5

```
S O R E C L E A N S E R
A U D E C T O
G I N S E N G Q U E L L
A I L U L E
C O N S I D E R A B L E
I Q X I A E
T A B U N P I N R E V
Y R E E T A
C O N S U L T A T I O N
C W C N R E
H I N G E F A C T O R S
E I N E E N C
F L E E T I N G H Y P E
```

Solution 6

```
S T O R M Y I I M P
R A A P R O N O
F I T T I N G O S W
V N L N O T E D E
D I S A L L O W A E
A A W C N R
A L U M N I M O U T H S
V N D G N E
E I S U R V I V A L
N I C H E E I R
U O V S U N R I S E
E R E E L S C A
S O N N R E L A Y S
```

SOLUTIONS

Solution 7

```
S T I N G Y   T E T H E R
O N U T   P   I     I
F A N C I E R   I F   D
T U L   I S S U I N G
E V E N T   B   T     E
N N   U   L I V E D
  D   B I L G E   A
E V O K E   A   N   A
A   A T   T O G A S
S A M U R A I   U   C
I A I   O U T D A T E
N N S N H R N
G L Y P H S   L E A D E D
```

Solution 8

```
W I P E   T R E S P A S S
O   A R   A   H   M   E
R E S C U E R   A L E R T
S S N   E   R   R   S
H I E R O G L Y P H I C
I   F   Y   T   C   G
P E T I T E   T O B A G O
S E H   F   N     V
  I N T E L L I G E N C E
S A M   A U   Y   R
H A N O I   G R E M L I N
U T L   O   D   O   E
N E S T L I N G   E N I D
```

Solution 9

```
C U C K O O   I   L   P
O   A   F U N N Y M A N
H A M   F   D R   Y
O   B A T E A U   I C O N
R E   R   C   C   F
T A R O T   R E L I E F S
    U   N   D S
S P O T T E D   S T A L E
  A   B   S A   P   L
L U L U   T O M A T O   I
  S R   E   A   G A S
M E S S A G E S   E   H
  D   T   G   S C H E M A
```

Solution 10

```
P U L P   F A R R I E R S
R   E   H   S   E X   U
E R A S E R S   P O P U P
C   K   A   U   R   U E
I V Y   V   M   O W N E R
P   M   Y I E L D   G   F
I   I   H     U   E   L
T   I   E T H I C     U
A O R T A   E   T   G O O
T   A   R   N   I   E U
I N G O T   R I O T E R S
O   E   E   Y   N   S L
N O S E D I V E   V E R Y
```

Solution 11

```
F A C T   P A S T R A M I
R   R   S   U   R   L N
E Q U A T O R   A T T I C
E   M   R   O   N   E O
Z E B R A   R O S T R U M
I   T   A   P   E   P
N O S H O W   H A N D L E
G   Y   S   S   R     T
P A R A P E T   E T U D E
O   I   H   R   N   S N
I M A G E   E N C R U S T
N   N   R   E   Y   A L
T R A V E S T Y   P L A Y
```

Solution 12

```
H I D E A W A Y   A M I R
A   O   C   D   T   A O
F I R T H   O   O U S T S
T   M   I   P   G   T E
    S E T T L E M E N T
F J V   S   T   R   T
L E A N E D   S H E L V E
A P M   S   E   Y   S
T R A J E C T O R Y
M   N   N U   N   A T
A G E N T   D   E N J O Y
T   S   S   I   S   A P
E P E E   C O N S T R U E
```

CROSSWORD

SOLUTIONS

Solution 13

```
  E L E C T R O N I C S
U   E   O   E   O   U   M
N   E M A C A W   B A A
S T R U M   E   I     S
U   Y   U   S   N E C K S
P H A N T A S M         P
P   N   E       N   B   R
O       A L T E R E G O   D
R U M B A   O   T   I   D
T   A   L   O   B I J O U
E A T   B U S T A   I   C
D   E   U E   L   N   E
  C R I M I N O L O G Y
```

Solution 14

```
D I A Z   T R A M W A Y S
I   S   I   E   U   R   O
A S H A M E D   L I S T S
L   E   P       T   E   O
O B S E R V A T I O N S
G       O   N   P   I   P
U M A   V I G I L   C O O
E   P   E   S   I       L
  D O G M A T I C A L L Y
B   S   E       I   U   M
L A T I N   P E T U N I A
O   L   T   A   Y   G   T
C R E O S O T E   M E S H
```

Solution 15

```
T A L C U M   A   S   G
E   A   A L S A T I A N
N U T   Z   K   U   N
D   E U R E K A   N O N E
O   S   S   N   T   E
N O T E S   S C R I P T S
    X   J   E   N
S T O P P E D   E G Y P T
  R   I   R   S   E   R
F A I R   S O C I A L   A
  S   I   E   R   L I D
T H A N K Y O U   E   E
  Y   G   S   B R I D E S
```

Solution 16

```
F J O R D S   S   S O B
  I   O   U N T I L   A
S T A T U E S   O   A B
  T   B   A   P E N N Y
H E R I T A G E   T   S
  R   F   E   C   E   I
A S Y L U M   P U N D I T
I   A   L   R   L   N
R   W   W O O D W O R M
D E N S E   Y   E   O
R   I   N   A U S T R A L
O   N A V A L   A   D
P I G   Y   A C C U S E
```

Solution 17

```
S O L U T I O N   T H O M
E   U   R   D   O   O   U
L I B Y A   D E L I M I T
L   B   N   E   I   A
    E   S   S U B U N I T
H A R I C O T   R   G   I
A       E   E       I   O
R   B   N   I T A L I A N
D R E A D E D   K   N
C   G   E   A   W   D
O R G A N Z A   B R A C E
P   A   L   L   R   E
Y A R N   A S C E N D E D
```

Solution 18

```
D R U I D   N O T H I N G
I   N   I   O   E   E
S   K   S   V   D R I E R
T H E M A T I C   O   D
R   M   V   C   F E A S T
I M P R O V E D   S   U
C   T   W       C   E   R
T   A   O N T H E J O B
S H O R E   U   I   E   U
  A   C   I N I M I C A L
R I G H T   C   E   T   E
  K   E   I   R   E   N
B U R R I T O   A U D I T
```

140

SOLUTIONS

CROSSWORD

Solution 19

C	A	S	T		S	P	E	C	I	O	U	S
R		I		C		L		I		S		T
Y	A	R	D	A	G	E		V	I	S	T	A
P		E		R		A		I		I		C
T	I	N	T		S		L	U	C	K	Y	
O			O	B	E	Y	S		L		F	
G		P		G			E		E		E	
R		L		R	U	M	E	R			R	
A	R	O	M	A		A		V		G	I	G
P		T		P		S		A		R		U
H	U	T	C	H		T	E	N	U	O	U	S
E		E		E		I		T		A		O
R	E	D	I	R	E	C	T		A	N	O	N

Solution 20

S	O	U	T	H	E	R	N		L	A	M	A
A		N		O		E			G		Q	
V	O	C	A	L		P	L	A	T	E	A	U
E		U		E			E		O		E	
		R		Y		A	N	N	E	L	I	D
H	A	L	F	W	I	T		O		D		U
O			O		O		S					C
T		B		O		O	U	T	P	O	S	T
E	C	U	A	D	O	R		A		N		
L		I			A		L		I		M	
I	L	L	I	C	I	T		G	O	O	S	E
E		D			O		O		N		S	
R	I	S	K		A	R	K	A	N	S	A	S

Solution 21

M	U	C	K		M	O	S	Q	U	I	T	O
U		R		D		W		U		C		A
S	P	A	N	I	E	L		E	L	E	C	T
I		M		C			S		C		H	
C	A	P	I	T	U	L	A	T	I	O	N	
I			A		I		I		L		A	
A	L	E		T	A	N	G	O		D	E	N
N		S		O		E		N			A	
	A	S	T	R	O	N	O	M	I	C	A	L
A		A		S			A		I		Y	
G	L	Y	P	H		R	E	R	E	D	O	S
A		E		I		H		K		E		E
R	E	D	E	P	L	O	Y		P	R	O	D

Solution 22

T	O	T	A	L	I	T	Y		A	P	E	D
A		U		U		H		I		I		O
T	O	X	I	C		R	E	C	L	A	I	M
E		E		R		I		N		N		E
		D		A		V	A	C	U	O	U	S
C	H	O	R	T	L	E		A		S		T
O			I			P		P				I
N		D		V		D	R	A	S	T	I	C
T	O	R	P	E	D	O		C		H		
E		Y		M			M		I		E		U
S	T	I	M	U	L	I		T	R	I	P	S
T		N			N		N		O		R		E
S	A	G	E		T	O	U	R	I	S	T	S

Solution 23

	L	I	G	H	T	M	I	N	D	E	D	
A		N		E		O		O		L		C
R		T		A	D	D	E	R		T	O	O
C	R	E	E	L		E		M		O		N
H		N		T		S		S	O	N	I	C
A	E	S	T	H	E	T	E					E
E		E		Y			P		O		A	
O				S	P	O	O	N	F	U	L	
L	O	L	L	Y		U		R		F		M
O		O		U		F		T	I	L	D	E
G	U	Y		M	U	F	T	I		O		N
Y		A		M		I		C		A		T
	P	L	A	Y	O	N	W	O	R	D	S	

Solution 24

T	Y	P	E	C	A	S	T		T	R	E	K
U		E		O		L		P		E		E
B	O	R	O	N		O		R	U	P	E	E
E		U		T		P		E		R		P
		P	R	O	P	E	R	T	I	E	S	
A		S		A		Y		E		S		A
T	R	I	A	D	S		S	Q	U	A	W	K
Y		G		I		G		U		L		E
P	E	N	I	C	I	L	L	I	N			
I		P		T		O		S		C		T
C	L	O	V	E		B		I	N	L	A	W
A		S		D		A		T		O		I
L	U	T	E		A	L	L	E	R	G	E	N

141

SOLUTIONS

Solution 25

```
I N T O   R E P U B L I C
N   R   F   R   N   E   O
E P I G R A M   D R A W N
X   E   I   I   E   K   F
P U R S E   N A R R A T E
E       N   E   A   G   C
R E S I D E   A C C E N T
I   T   L   I   H       I
E A R N I N G   I M A G O
N   E   N   N   E   B   N
C R E P E   O B V I A T E
E   T   S   R   E   S   R
D I S A S T E R   D E F Y
```

Solution 26

```
O V E R C A M E   B E A U
W   L   A   O   Q   N
E V I C T   R E S O U N D
D   C   A   A   A   E
    I   L   S I M I L A R
A C T I O N S   E   S   P
D       G       L       I
V   S   U   E M O T I O N
O S P R E Y S   D   D
C   R       T   R   L   V
A N A L Y S E   A R I S E
C   N       R   M   N   S
Y O G I   E S C A R G O T
```

Solution 27

```
  I N T O L E R A N C E
D   E   U   L   S   O   E
E   I   T H I C K   L U X
L O T U S   X   E   O   P
E   H   I   I   D O N O R
T W E E Z E R S       E
E   R   E   M   S   S
R       A D V A N C E S
I R O N S   U   R   A   I
O   U   E   R   C A N T O
U R N   T A B O O   D   N
S   C   U   A   N   A   S
  R E S P O N S I B L E
```

Solution 28

```
A N T E   E N S H R I N E
C   U   R   E   O   N   X
C O N V E N T   U N C U T
O   E   A   T   S   L   R
M A R   S   L   E V I T A
P       S L E E K   N   O
A   P   E       E   E   R
N   R   S I D L E       D
I T E M S   E   P   S K I
M   S   M   R   I   I   N
E X U D E   M I N U T I A
N   M   N   I   G   A   R
T R E A T I S E   P R A Y
```

Solution 29

```
C A V E   A D H E R E N T
O   I   S   I   X   L   E
M A G N U M S   P R I S M
P   G   B   U   E   S   P
A B O U T   S E R V I C E
S       E   E   I   O   R
S N E E R S   A M A N D A
I   S   R   A   E       M
O R P H A N S   N E R V E
N   O   N   I   T   E   N
A C U T E   D I A L E C T
T   S   A   E   L   V   A
E V E N N E S S   W E A L
```

Solution 30

```
R I V E T I N G   T R A P
I   E   R   I   A   L
M E N S A   G R A N T E E
S   E   U   G   H   A
    E   M   L A R D E R S
P E R V A D E   E   R   A
A       T       G       N
N   F   I   A B R E A S T
G L A N C E S   E   D
O   S       T   T   V   S
L U C K I E R   F R E S H
I   I       A   U   R   O
N E A R   S Y L L A B L E
```

SOLUTIONS

Solution 31

Solution 32

Solution 33

Solution 34

Solution 35

Solution 36

SOLUTIONS

Solution 37

```
M I N S T R E L     H E L D
I   E   E   N         C   I
F L A I R   T O R C H E S
F   T   R   A         O   A
    L   I   I C E B E R G
C R Y S T A L     X   S   R
O       O       C         E
X   P   R   E Q U A B L E
S T R A Y E D   L   I
W   O       I   P K L   L
A L M A N A C   A G I L E
I   P       T   T   N   E
N O T E   A S T E R I S K
```

Solution 38

```
T H E L M A     O   C   S
R   M     S U P P O R T S
A L I     K   P   N     A
C   G A Z E B O   F U R Y
E   R     W   S   U     E
D I E T S   S E A S I D E
        A   T   S   E
B O A R D E D   I S S U E
  C   T   N   N     T   D
M E A N   S K I N N Y   I
  L   E   I   G     M R S
F O R S O O T H     I   O
    T   S   N   T A V E R N
```

Solution 39

```
  R E C T A N G U L A R
I   X   A   S   P   A
N   P L A T C H   P A N
D R O O L   U   E   L   A
I   U   E   R   R H Y M E
F I N I S H E D       S
F   D   T       S   P   T
E         A L T H O U G H
R A T E D   E   A   R   E
E   A   E   A   L I S Z T
N I T   L E V E L   U   I
T   T   V   E   O   E   C
  T Y P E W R I T E R S
```

Solution 40

```
A C H Y   A C I D R A I N
I   A   P   A   I   N   O
R E V E R I E   S I N G E
L   O   E   S   T   U   S
I N C O M P A T I B L E
N   E   R   N   A   E
E S C U D O   S C O R E S
S   A   I   K   T       P
  U N A T T A I N A B L E
B   T   A   N   E   E   C
A D A P T   S A S H I M I
R   T   E   A   S   G   A
B R A N D I S H   T E L L
```

Solution 41

```
L A M B D A     Y   E B B
  N   R   B R O N X   R
A N A T O M Y   Y   P   A
  E   P   T   O D I U M
E X E M P T E D     A   B
  E   I   S   S   T   L
I S L A N D   A P I E C E
C   I   G   D   O     O
E   M     Y E A R N I N G
L E E C H   C   T     T
A   A   E   A V I G N O N
N   D E I T Y   N     R
D U E   R   I G N I T E
```

Solution 42

```
A R G O N   P L A T T E R
N   U   E   I     H   X
N   I   G   G   T U N I C
O U T D A T E D   M   S
Y   A   T   O   S P I T E
A G R E E I N G   S     X
N   S   D       S   S   E
C   A   D I D A C T I C
E V E R T   S   L   E   U
  E   M   D O C U M E N T
T I T A N   B   T   P   I
  L   D   A   E   L   V
A S S A Y E R   S I E G E
```

CROSSWORD

Solution 43

Solution 44

Solution 45

Solution 46

Solution 47

Solution 48

SOLUTIONS

Solution 49

```
D O L L O P . D . M . S
A A . A N I M A T O R .
I N N . I . A . C . L .
N . C H E R Y L . A L E C
T E . S . L . R . M . .
Y E T I S . R E J O I N S
. . D . T . D . N . . .
V E N E E R S . P I N E D
. X . A . A . U . O . R
D O L L . F O R B I D . A
. D . I . F . G . . D E W
S U N S H I N E . E . E
. S . T . C . D O D D E R
```

Solution 50

```
S A G S . B R I C K B A T
T . R . O . A . U . A . U
O V E R P A Y . R A N K S
M . A . P . . M . S . K .
A F T E R T H O U G H T .
C . . E . O . D . E . D
H A S . S H R U G . E M U
S . U . S . S . E . . T
. P R A I S E W O R T H Y
I . G . V . . N . I . F
T H E M E . H O L S T E R
C . O . L . O . Y . L . E
H O N E Y B E E . F E T E
```

Solution 51

```
A G A S S I . D . P . S
B . V . S H E R L O C K
A B I . L . N . A . O .
T . A R R E S T . T O T S
E R . . T . U . O . C .
D O Y E N . T R A N C H E
. . N . H . E . I . . .
T O D D L E R . S C U B A
. B . U . R . E . N . R
B E E R . B O X F U L . A
. Y . I . A . T . O R B
T E E N A G E R . . A . I
. D . G . E . A C I D I C
```

Solution 52

```
S I D E K I C K . S W A P
U . I . O . A . E . L
C O S T A . R E S I D U E
H . P . L . R . . G . A
. . E . A . O D D N E S S
H A L I B U T . E . S . U
O . . E . . . S . S . R
L . C . A . S U P R E M E
I N H E R I T . O . N .
N . U . . A . T . L . H
E M B A S S Y . I B I Z A
S . B . . E . S . S . I
S A Y S . O D O M E T E R
```

Solution 53

```
. N E V E R E N D I N G .
A . R . N . M . E . E . C
C . R . S K I M P . P I E
K H A K I . L . T . A . L
N . T . G . I . H A L V E
O R I E N T A L . . . . B
W . C . S . . . L . U . R
L . . . E T H I O P I A .
E L I O T . U . T . S . T
D . G . A . R . H E I D I
G E L . C A P R I . L . O
E . O . I . I . U . O . N
. C O N T E N T M E N T .
```

Solution 54

```
S A W S . O B L I G I N G
T . E . L . U . N . N . I
A N A L O G Y . C I T E S
R . R . N . . O . O . T .
D I S A G R E E M E N T .
U . . S . R . P . E . H
S I C . T I N G E . D R E
T . E . A . I . T . . A
. U N I N T E R E S T E D
A . T . D . . N . W . L
Q U A S I . T O C C A T A
U . U . N . O . Y . N . N
A B R O G A T E . A G E D
```

146

SOLUTIONS

Solution 55

Solution 56

Solution 57

Solution 58

Solution 59

Solution 60

SOLUTIONS

Solution 61

```
O D D S   C R E A T O R S
V   U S   U   M     T
E M B L E M S   T W I C E
R   A   L   T   H   T   A
S T I F F   E L E C T E D
T     E   D   N   E   F
A L B U M S   S T A D I A
T   A   P   A   I     S
E P S I L O N   C L I N T
M   T   O   D   A   O   N
E D I F Y   R E T I N U E
N   O   E   E   E   I   S
T O N E D E A F   A C E S
```

Solution 62

```
S P R I T Z     P   S T Y
  R   E   T R A I T   E
C O G E N C Y   I   U   A
  T   T   P   R E C U R
D E F E A T E D     K   N
  C   C   S   M   U   E
S T E A L S   J U M P E D
U   N   E   D   S     L
C   G     P A T H O G E N
C L A N G   M   R   C
U   G   A   P R O M P T S
M   E A R N S   O     O
B I D   Y     A M P E R E
```

Solution 63

```
I T S E L F   T H E S I S
N   C   I   B   O   P   C
S W E E P E R   L   I   U
I   N   I   O R D I N A L
S C A L D   A   A     P
T   R   D   L I G H T
    I   L O C A L   R
D R O N E   A     A   E
E     N   S   S I S A L
B R O U G H T   U   P   U
A   R   T   E M P T I E D
R   A   H   R   E   N   E
S P L A Y S   F R I G I D
```

Solution 64

```
S T R E A M     H   S P A
  E   P   E R U P T   D
T R A P P E D   N   A   V
  R   A   I   T H Y M E
F I D E L I T Y   I   R
  N   L   S   J   N   S
V E L V E T   B U N G E E
E   A   D   H   S   X
R   T   S E N T I N E L
D I T T Y   A   N   M
I   I   E   T H E R A P Y
C   C A T C H   S   T
T I E   I   A S S E S S
```

Solution 65

```
O P I N I O N S   E P I C
P   M   N   E     R   O
A P P L E   W E A P O N S
L   E   B   E   N   T
    D   R   S H I A T S U
C O E X I S T   N   O   M
A     A   T   E
B   O   T   E L E G I E S
B O R D E R S   R   M
A   G   T   C   P   R
G R A N O L A   E V E R Y
E   N   T   P   L   A
S A S H   J E T T I S O N
```

Solution 66

```
T E T C H Y   T O P P E D
A   R   E   C   U   U   E
B R A V A D O   T   P   P
L   N   V   M I L E A G E
E S S A Y   P   O     N
S   M   R   O W N E D
    I   S N E A K   O
E A T E N   S   T   J
N   O   S   F R A M E
S C H E R Z I   L   T   S
I   E   K   O C U L I S T
G   R   E   N   M   O   E
N E E D L E   O P E N E R
```

148

SOLUTIONS

Solution 67

```
T U G S   D E A F N E S S
R R   D   L   I   R   H
I S O T O P E   S A U N A
A   O   I   V   H   D   M
L I M I T   E X A M I N E
A       Y   N   N   T   L
N E E S O N   A D H E R E
D   A   U   E   C       S
E A R D R U M   H O O D S
R   L   S   P   I   V   N
R A I S E   I M P R O V E
O   E   L   R   S   I   S
R A R E F I E D   O D E S
```

Solution 68

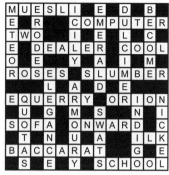

```
M U E S L I   E   D   B
E   R     C O M P U T E R
T W O     I   E   L   C
E   D E A L E R   C O O L
O   E     Y   A   I   M
R O S E S   S L U M B E R
    L   A   D   E
E Q U E R R Y   O R I O N
  U   G   M   S   N   I
S O F A   O N W A R D   C
  T   N   U   A   I L K
B A C C A R A T   G   E
  S   E   Y   S C H O O L
```

Solution 69

```
C A S H   D E V I L I S H
O   A   H   R   N   M   A
R A U C O U S   T R A I L
R   D   M   A   E   G   F
E L I D E   T A R N I S H
S       L   Z   M   N   E
P A R C E L   G E N E V A
O   E   S   B   D       R
N A T A S H A   I N A P T
D   R   N   F   A   W   E
I R A T E   F O R W A R D
N   I   S   L   Y   R   L
G A N G S T E R   E D G Y
```

Solution 70

```
S H I R T Y   C R O C U S
O   N   E   M   E   A   P
R O T U N D A   P   L   R
T   A   S   G O R I L L A
E A G L E   I   O       I
D   L     S   V E G A N
    I   L I T H E   U
F L O R A   E     L   E
A     U   R   P A L E R
C H I A N T I   E   I   E
I   R   D   A C E R B I C
N   A   E   L   L   L   T
G E N T R Y   U S H E R S
```

Solution 71

```
O B O E S   B E T W E E N
V   R   M   O     A   X
E G A   N   W I R E R
R E A S S E S S   V   R
P   N   H   A   J E T T Y
O L I V E O I L   R   A
W   C   S     T   R   R
E   D   B E F R I E N D
R A D A R   R   E   T   S
  P   M   M A R M O S E T
R A M P S   S   O   I   I
  R   E     E   R   N   C
S T A R T E R   S P A N K
```

Solution 72

```
C O L A   E M I G R A T E
O   U   A   O   O   Z   T
L A N O L I N   L E A R N
O   A   L   T   D   L   A
S T R A I G H T E N E R
S   M   S   N   A   A
A C C E P T   R E A S O N
L   H   O   C   A       G
  S A C R I L E G I O U S
G   L   T   O   L   C   T
E L I Z A   S W E L T E R
M   C   N   E   S   E   O
S W E E T E S T   I T E M
```

149

CROSSWORD

SOLUTIONS

Solution 73

Solution 74

Solution 75

Solution 76

Solution 77

Solution 78

CROSSWORD

Solution 79

Solution 80

Solution 81

Solution 82

Solution 83

Solution 84

SOLUTIONS

Solution 85

```
A V E R S I O N ▮ M A L ▮ I
I ▮ L ▮ P ▮ U ▮ ▮ ▮ V ▮ M
L E D G E ▮ T O U R I S M
S ▮ E ▮ L ▮ L ▮ ▮ ▮ A ▮ O
▮ ▮ S ▮ L ▮ E X I S T E D
U N T W I S T ▮ N ▮ E ▮ E
N ▮ ▮ ▮ N ▮ ▮ ▮ N ▮ ▮ ▮ S
I ▮ I ▮ G ▮ E G O T I S T
F O C U S E D ▮ C ▮ N
O ▮ I ▮ ▮ ▮ I ▮ E ▮ T ▮ R
R E C R U I T ▮ N I E C E
M ▮ L ▮ ▮ ▮ O ▮ C ▮ N ▮ L
S E E P ▮ A R D E N T L Y
```

Solution 86

```
▮ P E R F O R M A N C E ▮
A ▮ X ▮ L ▮ E ▮ L ▮ L ▮ D
L P ▮ I D E A L ▮ A D O
T U L I P ▮ K ▮ E ▮ I ▮ W
E ▮ O ▮ P ▮ E ▮ Y E M E N
R E D H E A D S ▮ ▮ ▮ ▮ T
C ▮ E ▮ D ▮ ▮ S ▮ D ▮ R
A ▮ ▮ ▮ N E U T R I N O
T U B E S ▮ Y ▮ E ▮ V ▮ D
I ▮ E ▮ T ▮ R ▮ T R E N D
O F F ▮ E M I T S ▮ R ▮ E
N ▮ O ▮ E ▮ E ▮ O ▮ T ▮ N
▮ A G E L E S S N E S S ▮
```

Solution 87

```
A S T U T E ▮ B ▮ S ▮ K
I ▮ I ▮ ▮ G R E E T I N G
R U T ▮ R ▮ H ▮ R ▮ I
B ▮ B O D E G A ▮ A L G A
U ▮ I ▮ T ▮ V ▮ T ▮ H
S A T Y R ▮ R E L E N T S
▮ ▮ A ▮ C ▮ D ▮ G
P R O C U R E ▮ M Y T H S
▮ U ▮ H ▮ E ▮ S ▮ U ▮ P
L E S T ▮ A T T A I N ▮ R
▮ F ▮ I ▮ T ▮ A ▮ D U O
T U R N C O A T ▮ R ▮ U
▮ L ▮ G ▮ R ▮ E R R A N T
```

Solution 88

```
T A K I N G ▮ S H A P E D
I ▮ I ▮ O ▮ P ▮ A ▮ L ▮ O
C O N F I D E ▮ L ▮ E ▮ I
K ▮ G ▮ S ▮ R E F R A I N
E N S U E ▮ M ▮ W ▮ ▮ ▮ G
R ▮ H ▮ I ▮ A C H E S
▮ ▮ I ▮ M U S H Y ▮ E
A L P H A ▮ S ▮ ▮ ▮ E ▮ L
L ▮ ▮ R ▮ I ▮ M I D G E
B A T H T U B ▮ O ▮ L ▮ A
I ▮ I ▮ I ▮ L I O N E S S
N ▮ E ▮ N ▮ E ▮ R ▮ S ▮ E
O R D A I N ▮ S E N S E D
```

Solution 89

```
B O O K C A S E ▮ C A T S
U ▮ W ▮ O ▮ C ▮ C ▮ N ▮ O
G L E N S ▮ R ▮ O U T E R
S ▮ N ▮ M ▮ A ▮ N ▮ I ▮ C
▮ ▮ ▮ C O M P A T I B L E
C ▮ V ▮ P ▮ S ▮ R ▮ O ▮ R
O R I S O N ▮ R I D D L E
I ▮ N ▮ L ▮ G ▮ B ▮ Y ▮ R
F I C T I T I O U S
F ▮ I ▮ T ▮ N ▮ T ▮ A ▮ C
U M B R A ▮ G ▮ I M P L Y
R ▮ L ▮ N ▮ E ▮ O ▮ E ▮ A
E Y E S ▮ G R A N D S O N
```

Solution 90

```
B A G S ▮ S P A C I O U S
E ▮ E ▮ A ▮ O ▮ A ▮ N ▮ E
A N T I G E N ▮ R E G A L
S ▮ U ▮ R ▮ C ▮ B ▮ O ▮ F
T O P ▮ I ▮ H ▮ O P I N E
O ▮ ▮ ▮ C L O T H ▮ N ▮ V
F ▮ A ▮ U ▮ ▮ ▮ Y ▮ G ▮ I
B ▮ B ▮ L U C I D ▮ ▮ ▮ D
U P S E T ▮ O ▮ R ▮ S E E
R ▮ E ▮ U ▮ C ▮ A ▮ C ▮ N
D I N A R ▮ O U T M O S T
E ▮ C ▮ A ▮ O ▮ E ▮ R ▮ L
N E E D L I N G ▮ D E N Y
```

CROSSWORD

Solution 91

```
E P O X Y   M A T I N E E
X   L   I   Y   M   X
P   I   E   O   S P A T E
E N V E L O P E   A   O
N   I   D   I   V I L L A
S K E L E T A L   R   M
I   R   D     I   S   E
V   A   P L A N K T O N
E X I L E   I   N   R   D
  E   M   A Q U A R I U M
A N I O N   U   R   D   E
  O   S   O   D   E   N
A N O T H E R   S P R A T
```

Solution 92

```
G A S H   E S S E N C E S
L   T   O   A   M   L   I
A R R I V A L   P L A I N
C   A   E   O   H   M   E
I M P E R S O N A T O R
E     I   N   T   U   A
R E C A N T   C I T R I C
S   O   D   S   C     A
  I L L U S T R A T I O N
I   L   L   O   L   N   T
D O I N G   D E L I L A H
E   D   E   G   Y   A   U
A B E R D E E N   G Y M S
```

Solution 93

```
M U L E   A S T O N I S H
A   A   W   U   B   N   E
G I N G H A M   L E G A L
I   C   O   M   I   R   T
S M E L L   E X T R E M E
T     E   D   E   S   R
E P O C H S   E R A S E S
R   V   E   S   A     K
I N E X A C T   T A B L E
A   R   R   O   I   O   L
L E A S T   L O O K O U T
L   W   E   E   N   K   E
Y I E L D I N G   T S A R
```

Solution 94

```
O A S T   B L A C K T I E
F   P   N   E   O   H   C
F L A T O U T   N E I G H
I   I   N   T   S   N   O
C O N V A L E S C E N T
E     L   R   R   E   A
R O C O C O   C I R R U S
S   O   O   T   P     S
  U N C H A R I T A B L E
O   D   O   U   I   L   S
S P O O L   C L O S E T S
L   N   I   K   N   A   O
O V E R C A S T   S T A R
```

Solution 95

```
S E S A M E   H A R D E N
H   T   U   P   B   E   O
Y O U N G E R   Y   M   U
I   N   G   O U S T I N G
N A N N Y   B   S     A
G   I     L   A S S E T
    N   S P E L L   O
O U G H T   M     N   C
N     A   A   S M I T H
R E A D M I T   I   N   E
U   P   I   I N S U L A R
S   S   N   C   Q   A   U
H Y E N A S   C O B W E B
```

Solution 96

```
P R O V I S O S   S C A M
E   U   N   B   C   L   A
C A R A T   J   O V E N S
K   S   E   E   N   R   T
      B L A C K S M I T H
P   A   L   T   T   C   E
R E P A I D   C I C A D A
O   O   G   M   T   L   D
F A S T I D I O U S
F   T   B   L   E   W   D
E M A I L   I   N U R S E
R   T   E   E   C   E   W
S E E M   B U O Y A N C Y
```

SOLUTIONS

Solution 97

```
. D I S S O L U T I O N .
D R A . O H V . C . . .
I K . P I L A U . E A U
S U S H I . L M R . T .
I . O E . P A S T A . N
L E M O N A D E . . . .
L . E T . . M . S D . .
U . . F A M I S H E D .
S I F T S . U D . I R .
I . A W T . T E M P I .
O D D . E L U D E . M E
N . E A M . R E D . . .
. A S T R O N O M E R S
```

Solution 98

```
D O D O . S A T I A T E D
I . E . M N . N . R . I
F A L L A C Y . E V A N S
F . H . S . H . X . N A
E P I C S . O P P O S E D
R . . P . W . E . O V
E X H O R T . C R I M E A
N . E . O . A . I . . N
T I R A D E S . E R E C T
I . E . U . T . N V . A
A Z T E C . E T C H I N G
T . I . R . R . E L . E
E N C O D I N G . U S E D
```

Solution 99

```
M A C R O . T Y R A N T S
A . O . S U . U . E . R
G N . T . S . D R A Y S
N O T E L E S S . I . S
E . O . E . L . M A L T A
S Q U I R R E L . L . G
I . R . S . . O . R G
U . . O . R E A P P E A R
M O T T O . X . T . C E
. U . I . L I A I S O N S
S T R O P . S . C . I S
. E . S . T . A . L O
A N G E L U S . L O S E R
```

Solution 100

```
P R O T E I N S . E L K S
O . G . I . U . . O . T
L U R I D . D I P L O M A
E . E . E . G . . F . N
. . S . R . E N G L A N D
B E S I D E S . R . H A
A . . O . . . A . . R
D . N . W . A D V I S E D
G R O A N E D . I . A
E . B . . O . T . L . B
R O O S T E R . A G A T E
E . D . . N . T . M . V
D A Y S . A S P E R I T Y
```

Solution 101

```
C U R L . C L A P P I N G
H . U . E . U . L . G . U
A L L E L E S . A N N O Y
R . E . E . T . I . I . S
I N D O C T R I N A T E .
S . . T . E . S . E . G
M I S E R Y . L A R D E R
A . C . O . A . I . . E
. H A P P Y G O L U C K Y
G . L . L . E . I . A . N
O P E R A . I G N O B L E
B . N . T . N . G . A . S
I C E B E R G S . A L P S
```

Solution 102

```
S C A R F S . A T O N A L
T . D . U . O . O . E . E
E N D E M I C . K . R . S
P . I . E . C R A Y O N S
P U T T S . U . M . . E
E . I . . P . A S T E R
. . O . C H A L K . R
P U N C H . T . . E . A
O . . E . I . V I A L S
S I R O C C O . A . S . P
T . O . K . N E P T U N E
A . S . I . S . I . R . C
L A Y I N G . A D V E R T
```

154

CROSSWORD (vertical, right margin)

Solution 103

```
I V O R █ U N I C Y C L E
N N █ F I █ O █ O L
S T I R R U P █ V O W E L
E █ O █ U █ E █ S █ E
C O N V I N C I N G L Y █
U █ █ T █ A █ T █ I B
R A P █ F L I N G █ P R O
E █ A U R A █ D
█ B I B L I O G R A P H Y
D N N █ D I W
R I F L E █ O R E G A N O
O U S L N N R
P A L I S A D E █ S O A K
```

Solution 104

```
I N F E R █ A N T H I L L
N █ L E █ L █ A █ O
S █ O F F █ L █ A R S O N
U N C T U O U S █ A █ S
R █ K █ S █ R █ A S H E N
G R E N A D E S █ S █ O
E █ D █ L █ F █ P █ R
N █ O █ E M P O R I U M
T H E F T █ A █ R █ A
█ A █ F █ T R I B U N A L
E S S E X █ I █ I █ I T
█ T █ R █ N █ D █ I T
E Y E S O R E █ S C A R Y
```

Solution 105

```
█ P L A Y I N G C A R D █
I █ E █ T █ I █ U █ E W
N A █ T E M P T █ A A H
A L D E R █ B █ U █ M E
D █ I █ I █ U █ P A S T E
V A N Q U I S H █ █ █ L
E █ G █ M █ C █ P █ B
R █ █ P A N O R A M A
T A K E S █ M █ M █ R █
E █ E █ T █ O █ P A T E R
N I B █ A R E N A █ N █ O
T █ A █ R █ B █ C █ E W
█ A B S T R A C T A R T
```

Solution 106

```
D E B T █ P U S S Y C A T
E █ E █ H █ N █ W █ A █ E
D E S P O I L █ I M B U E
I █ O █ P █ O █ M █ I █ N
C O M M E N C E M E N T █
A █ █ L █ K █ I █ E █ T
T A S T E D █ U N I T E S
E █ A █ S █ D █ G █ █ U
█ S U B S C R I P T I O N
A █ S █ N █ O █ O █ D █ A
C R A N E █ P R O B L E M
H █ G █ S █ I █ L █ E █ I
E V E N S O N G █ O R B S
```

Solution 107

```
T O W E L S █ P █ A █ F
S █ I █ N A U T I C A L
H I S █ A █ R █ R █ C
I █ H I C C U P █ B A I T
R █ E █ K █ O █ R █ L
T O D A Y █ A S S U M E D
█ █ N █ C █ E █ S
U P S T A R T █ G H O U L
█ R █ E █ U █ A █ Y █ A
C O M A █ E N V I E S █ I
█ T █ T █ L █ E █ T O R
D E S E R T E R █ E █ D
█ M █ R █ Y █ T H E R M S
```

Solution 108

```
C A P E █ S P E A K I N G
L █ L █ S █ A █ R █ M █ O
U N U S U A L █ R A P I D
M █ M █ P █ A █ U █ S
S U B S E Q U E N T L Y █
I █ █ R █ N █ G █ S █ M
E L L █ N A C R E █ E T A
R █ I █ A █ L █ M █ █ N
█ O F F T H E R E C O R D
A █ T █ U █ N █ V █ A
F R I A R █ O U T W E A R
A █ N █ A █ U █ S █ R █ I
R E G U L A R S █ E T O N
```

SOLUTIONS

Solution 109

```
C O W E R S . . Y . N . S
L H . . C L E M E N C Y
E V E . A . A . G . H
R . E A R N E R . A G E S
I Z . T . D . T . M
C R E S T . N O T I C E D
. Q . N . T . O
S C O U R E R . I N A N E
. O . A . M . B . . B . R
A M E N . E N I G M A . R
. B . D . S . N . . T E A
W A V E R I N G . . E . T
. T . R . S . O D E S S A
```

Solution 110

```
D R E A M . G R O W N U P
O . N . Y . U . R . P
U D L . I . I . R E A P S
B A G U E T T E . N . E
T . A . E . A . S C A R F
L U M I N A R Y . H . R
E . E . E . K . G . I
S . . C . B L I N K I N G
S P O O F . O . I . R . H
. O . B . P O I G N A N T
O S C A R . M . H . F . E
. E . L . E . T . F . N
P R E T E N D . S E E D S
```

Solution 111

```
H O U N D S . S A L T E D
O . N . E . C . C . A . E
V I B R A T O . C . U . C
E . U . L . M I L I T I A
R A C E S . B . A . . . N
S . K . I . . I N E R T
. . L . D E N I M . M
A D E L E . A . . . B . B
N . . M . T . S C O U R
N A I R O B I . C . L . E
A . S . T . O V E R D U E
L . L . I . N . N . E . Z
S C A R C E . B E A N I E
```

Solution 112

```
R E S T . M A N D O L I N
I . P . S . G . I . U . E
C R U M P L E . S A M B A
O . R . R . N . C . B . T
C O N V E N T I O N A L
H . . A . S . U . G . C
E N C O D E . A R D O U R
T . A . E . T . A . . E
. C L E A R S I G H T E D
S . C . G . E . I . H . I
T W I L L . T A N G E N T
I . U . E . S . G . R . O
R E M E D I E S . O M A R
```

Solution 113

```
. P R E D E C E S S O R
O . E . A . A . T . D . D
V . T . M I C R O . D I E
E Q U I P . H . I . L . H
R . R . I . E . C O Y L Y
B A N K N O T E . . . . D
E . S . G . . . F . C . R
A . . . A U T O M A T A
R A C E D . G . X . R . T
I . O . E . A . H A I T I
N O R . B A N J O . B . O
G . G . U . D . L . O . N
. D I S G R A C E F U L
```

Solution 114

```
S O F T . E N C U M B E R
A . R . M . I . N . E . O
P R O S A I C . F L A P S
I . T . N . E . A . G . E
E X H A U S T I V E L Y
N . . F . Y . O . E . E
C R A V A T . N U R S E S
E . M . C . G . R . . P
. P I T T E R P A T T E R
E . A . U . E . B . H . E
D E B A R . B U L L E T S
I . L . E . E . E . T . S
T H E O R I S E . H A L O
```

SOLUTIONS

Solution 115

I	D	I	O	M	S			E		A	G	O
	A			I		U	N	D	E	R		C
I	N	F	A	N	T	S		D		M		T
	I			O		U		Y	A	H	O	O
D	E	M	E	R	A	R	A			O		P
	L			I		P		S		L		U
A	S	S	E	T	S		S	W	E	E	T	S
R		U		Y		I		I			A	
S		B			I	N	U	N	D	A	T	E
E	A	S	E	S		C		D			T	
N		I		I		U	N	L	O	V	E	D
A		D	E	T	E	R		E			R	
L	Y	E		E			G	R	O	U	S	E

Solution 116

P	O	R	E		M	O	T	H	B	A	L	L
L		O		D		T		I		N		E
A	R	M	R	E	S	T		P	A	G	E	S
Y		E		L		A		P		U		S
B	O	O	G	I	E	W	O	O	G	I	E	
A				C		A		P		S		E
C	A	S	U	A	L		G	O	T	H	A	M
K		H		T		D		T				I
	D	E	R	E	G	U	L	A	T	I	O	N
G		R		S		L		M		V		E
L	O	B	E	S		C	A	U	T	I	O	N
A		E		E		E		S		E		C
D	E	T	O	N	A	T	E		A	S	H	E

Solution 117

S	W	A	R	M	S			S		B	O	A
	A			O		O	T	T	E	R		L
A	D	O	R	N	E	D		U		A		I
	D			A		O		B	E	I	N	G
G	L	A	S	S	F	U	L			L		N
	E			T		R		A		L		E
E	S	P	R	I	T		A	G	R	E	E	D
N		E		C		B		L			Y	
S		L			M	O	D	I	F	I	E	D
U	S	I	N	G		R		T			B	
R		C		E		A	C	T	U	A	R	Y
E		A	N	N	E	X		E			O	
S	U	N		E			A	R	R	O	W	S

Solution 118

L	I	F	E	B	O	A	T		L	E	E	R
I		I		O		R				U		E
M	E	T	R	O		C	A	S	T	L	E	S
E		T		K		A				O		I
		E		M		D	E	M	I	G	O	D
M	E	D	I	A	T	E		A		Y		U
E				K				C				A
G		A		E		U	N	R	A	V	E	L
A	L	S	O	R	A	N		O		E		
L		H				I		C		R		E
I	S	O	B	A	R	S		O	X	B	O	W
T		R				E		S		A		E
H	O	E	S		E	X	E	M	P	L	A	R

Solution 119

I	N	C	E		S	C	O	R	C	H	E	S
N		R		E		L		E		A		P
A	N	I	M	A	T	E		P	U	P	I	L
P		M		U		V		O		L		E
P	A	P		D		E		S	K	E	I	N
R				E	A	R	L	S		S		D
O		T		C				E		S		I
P		O		O	V	A	L	S				F
R	E	P	E	L		B		S		A	C	E
I		M		O		R		I		M		R
A	L	O	N	G		A	V	O	C	A	D	O
T		S		N		D		N		Z		U
E	S	T	E	E	M	E	D		L	E	G	S

Solution 120

G	R	I	N	D	I	N	G		C	H	U	B
A		B		I		A		A		O		U
G	R	E	Y	S		P		N	O	O	K	S
S		X		H		K		T		L		I
			D	E	D	I	C	A	T	I	O	N
S		E		A		N		G		G		E
U	T	T	E	R	S		C	O	R	A	L	S
R		C		T		C		N		N		S
F	A	H	R	E	N	H	E	I	T			
A		I		N		U		S		D		I
C	A	N	O	E		K		T	H	U	M	B
E		G		D		K		I		E		I
D	E	S	K		C	A	L	C	U	L	U	S

SOLUTIONS

Solution 121

```
S I C K L E   S   E   M
E   O     D I C A P R I O
E L F   D   R   I   C
S   F A M I N E   D A R E
A   E   E   E   E   O
W A R P S   O D D M E N T
    U   U   S   I
O F F L I N E   O C E A N
  L   L   H S   X   E
L I M B   A L K A L I   R
  G   A   P   U   L I V
C H I C K P E A   E   E
  T   K   Y   S E N S E S
```

Solution 122

```
A L S O   B R O C C O L I
U   T   P   O   I   R   L
T R E M O L O   R E B E L
H   M   S   T   C   I   U
O N S E T   E Q U A T E S
R   G   D   M   A   T
I N B O R N   O S T L E R
S   R   A   A   C   A
A V O I D E D   R E B U T
T   A   U   D   I   A   I
I N D I A   E M B A R G O
O   E   T   R   E   G   N
N O N S E N S E   E E L S
```

Solution 123

```
S U D S   B U D D H I S M
L   I   D   P   I   M   I
E A S T E N D   S E P A L
E   C   C   A   C   L   K
P R O P O R T I O N A L
E   N   E   U   N   P
R E S I G N   G R O T T O
S   T   E   E   T   N
  C O N S I S T E N T L Y
S   R   T   C   O   H   T
K O A L A   A Q U A R I A
I   G   N   P   S   E   I
T H E A T R E S   Z E A L
```

Solution 124

```
S I C K   P A N D E M I C
U   L   R   M   I   I   O
I N A N E L Y   S E L L S
T   R   F   I   K   Y
C H E E R F U L N E S S
A   E   N   G   O   N
S A P   S M I T E   P S I
E   E   H   O   N   T
  I N D I A N S U M M E R
K   S   N   O   O   O
I C I N G   H O U S I N G
E   O   L   E   S   S   E
V I N E Y A R D   S T U N
```

Solution 125

```
D O C T O R   O B L O N G
A   U   M   P   U   V   A
T A B L E A U   I   I   N
I   I   G   B U L L D O G
V A C U A   L   D   E
E   L   I   E T H O S
  E   O C C U R   A
A E S O P   H   N   D
L   H   O   D A D D Y
P A R V E N U   E   M   N
I   U   L   S U L T A N A
N   S   I   E   T   D   M
E N T R A P   M A K E D O
```

Solution 126

```
B A C K S E A T   B E D E
E   H   T   V   C   V   L
S H E E R   E   A B A T E
T   R   A   R   B   L   V
      D I S T R I B U T E
S   F   G   S   N   A   N
T R O P H Y   S E X T E T
U   O   T   A   T   E   H
B O T H E R S O M E
B   B   N   T   A   M   A
O V A T E   H   K N E A D
R   L   D   M   E   E   D
N I L E   N A R R A T E S
```

CROSSWORD

Solution 127

S	I	T	S		S	T	A	R	T	E	R	S
T		R		F	I		E		L		L	
E	P	I	S	O	D	E		P	A	U	S	E
P		L		R		R		R		S		I
P	I	L	O	T		E	V	E	N	I	N	G
I			U		D		S		O		H	
N	I	T	W	I	T		P	E	A	N	U	T
G		Y		T		S		N			O	
S	U	P	P	O	R	T		T	H	I	E	F
T		I		U		A		I		T		H
O	A	S	I	S		P	A	N	A	C	E	A
N		T		L		E		G		H		N
E	S	S	A	Y	I	S	T		D	Y	E	D

Solution 128

I	N	V	E	R	S	E	S		C	R	E	W
N		E		I		M	E		E		E	
C	H	I	N	O		I		N	E	A	R	S
H		L		D		N		T		W		T
			D	E	C	E	L	E	R	A	T	E
M		A		J		M		R		K		R
U	N	S	E	A	T		S	T	R	E	W	N
L		S		N		I		A		N		S
B	R	I	D	E	S	M	A	I	D			
E		S		I		P		N		D		A
R	O	T	O	R		A		I	D	O	L	S
R		E		O		L		N		U		K
Y	O	D	A		L	A	G	G	A	R	D	S

Solution 129

E	B	B	S		H	I	S	P	A	N	I	C
V		O		I		C		R		O		L
E	S	S	E	N	C	E		O	R	I	B	I
R		U		T		B		V		S		V
L	I	N	E	R		O	R	I	F	I	C	E
A			A		X		D		E		A	
S	E	C	O	N	D		N	E	U	R	O	N
T		H		S		H		N			D	
I	N	A	N	I	T	Y		T	E	A	S	E
N		N		G		B		I		P		R
G	E	N	R	E		R	E	A	C	H	E	S
L		E		N		I		L		I		O
Y	U	L	E	T	I	D	E		E	D	E	N

Solution 130

W	H	I	M		E	M	U	L	A	T	O	R
R		N		M		A		I		E		I
A	S	T	O	U	N	D		C	A	M	E	L
N		R		L		A		K		P		L
G	O	O	D	T	E	M	P	E	R	E	D	
L			I		E		T		R		R	
E	X	P	E	L	S		G	Y	R	A	T	E
S		R		I		A		S			C	
	C	O	R	N	I	S	H	P	A	S	T	Y
H		V		G		S		L		W		C
A	D	I	E	U		I	N	I	T	I	A	L
S		S		A		S		T		S		E
P	R	O	C	L	A	I	M		A	S	P	S

Solution 131

T	A	L	E		S	C	R	I	B	B	L	E
H		L		L		R		N		O		F
E	M	A	N	A	T	E		S	C	O	F	F
S		M		B		A		U		K		E
I	T	A	L	Y		M	U	F	F	L	E	R
X			R		Y		F		E		V	
T	R	I	V	I	A		C	E	N	T	R	E
H		V		N		G		R			S	
S	C	O	O	T	E	R		A	S	P	I	C
E		R		H		A		B		L		E
N	T	I	N	I		V	I	L	L	A	I	N
S		E		N		E		E		T		C
E	A	S	T	E	R	L	Y		N	E	V	E

Solution 132

C	A	M	P		S	P	R	I	T	Z	E	R
O		A		H		E		N		E		O
N	A	R	R	O	W	S		C	R	A	W	L
F		G		U		E		O		L		L
I	C	E		S		T		N	O	O	S	E
G			E	X	A	M	S		U		R	
U		A		O			I		S		C	
R		C		F	L	A	G	S			O	
A	U	R	A	L		N		T		L	E	A
T		O		O		O		E		I		S
I	N	N	E	R		R	I	N	G	L	E	T
O		Y		D		A		T		A		E
N	A	M	E	S	A	K	E		S	C	A	R

SOLUTIONS

CROSSWORD

Solution 133

M	A	N	D	A	T	E	S		F	I	R	M
A		E		N	X		U		N		O	
S	P	O	O	N		O		N	O	V	E	L
K		N		O	T		D		A		A	
		B	U	S	I	N	E	S	S	E	S	
S		L		N	C		T		I		S	
P	R	I	N	C	E		O	E	U	V	R	E
R		G	E		F		C	E			S	
I	N	N	U	M	E	R	A	T	E			
N		E	E		I		A	G		S		
K	N	O	W	N		G		B	E	L	O	W
L		U		T		H		L		E	O	
E	A	S	T		S	T	E	E	P	E	S	T

Solution 134

M	I	F	F	E	D		C	R	A	B	B	Y
Y		O	N		I		E		O		O	
S	I	X	T	E	E	N		P		O		D
T		H	M		T	R	U	S	T	E	E	
I	V	O	R	Y		E		L			L	
C		L			R		S	I	D	E	S	
		E		G	O	R	S	E		E		
I	B	S	E	N		O			L		E	
N			O		G		L	Y	I	N	G	
D	E	A	D	S	E	A		A		R		R
O		X		T		T	O	P	S	I	D	E
O		E		I		E		S		U		S
R	E	D	U	C	E		L	E	M	M	A	S

160